Map of
County, Idaho

...arpment of the
...hee Plateau

Scale: |_____ 30 miles _____|

Clover Flat

Bruneau

Desert

Bruneau R.

Murphy Hot Springs

...hee Creek

Washington

Oregon

Idaho

Owyhee County

Don Fritts

9-16-57

OWYHEE:
THE LIFE OF A NORTHERN DESERT

OWYHEE:
The Life of a Northern Desert

By

EARL J. LARRISON

ILLUSTRATED BY DON FRITTS

THE CAXTON PRINTERS, LTD.
CALDWELL, IDAHO
1957

Printed and bound in the United States of America by
The CAXTON PRINTERS, Ltd.
Caldwell, Idaho
79091

To those valiant men and women whose
faith and courage made a home
of sand and sagebrush

Acknowledgments

Books such as this are not made by one man alone but are the final result of the work of many hands. Accordingly, the writer thanks the following persons who have aided in the prosecution of the Owyhee Project and in the preparation of this book:

Dr. Louis C. Cady, dean of the Graduate School, University of Idaho, and Dr. Harold McIlvaine, former head, Department of Biological Sciences, University of Idaho, for administrative assistance in General Research Project G-6 of which the present book is a partial result; Dr. H. Walter Steffens, executive dean, University of Idaho, for his long and continued interest in the field activities of the Department of Biological Sciences; Osborne E. Casey, the late Osborne E. Casey, Sr., Dr. Malcolm T. Jollie, Dr. Johnson Parker, Martel Morache, and Chet Higman for field assistance; Dr. William H. Baker, head, Department of Biological Sciences, for field and botanical aid; the many Owyhee County residents who have helped in numerous ways; and particularly to Harry W. Higman for his considerable assistance in field work and in the preparation of the book.

The writer takes especial pleasure in thanking Don Fritts, former Graduate Assistant in Zoology, University of Idaho, and now Parasitologist at Montana State College, whose artistic talents and interest have gone a long way in contributing to the attractiveness of this volume.

Gratitude is due the Hudson's Bay Record Society, London, for permission to quote from Peter Skene Ogden's Snake River Country Journals.

And finally, appreciation should be given James H. Gipson, Sr., and Gordon Gipson of The Caxton Printers, Ltd., for their many courtesies during the printing and publishing of OWYHEE: THE LIFE OF A NORTHERN DESERT.

EARL J. LARRISON

Table of Contents

Introduction

Transitions between desert and irrigated land are often abrupt but I have never seen so striking a change from luxuriant lushness to arid harshness as is found in a drive south from Nampa, Idaho. I start in a land of plenty where onions grow in fields so large that their odor is everywhere. Potatoes produce with a bounteousness that justifies the claim once made on the state's auto license plates—"World Famous Potato." Alfalfa and corn prosper as such crops can thrive only when raised on fertile and well-watered soil. Haystacks, large and closely spaced, fine houses, well-maintained barns, and tidy lanes all show the wealth and productiveness of the area.

But before I have traveled over the eighteen-mile stretch south to the Snake River, I pass the end of the irrigated section. Beyond the Snake the hard-surfaced road is the one mark of modernity in a desert which embraces, except for a few strips bordering the mountain streams and the mountain highlands, all of Owyhee, the southwest county of Idaho. The deep, fertile green of the farming country has ceased as grass stops at the edge of flagstones on a lawn. Browns and grays begin to dominate, and only small clumps of grass and other vegetation have a foothold. The vistas within the irrigation limits are shortened by lines of trees raised for protection, but there are no such windbreaks beyond the Snake. Instead, great light-colored patches mark the miles of ancient lake beds which lie between dark masses of rock of the higher levels. Cliffs and odd-shaped mounds project here and there with an irregularity which makes a spectator feel he is looking at a scene of confusion and disorderliness. Mountain ranges stand in the distance, the lower elevations dry, brown, and smooth, their upper flanks roughened by growing shrubs and trees, and their peaks, if high enough, striped with banks of summer snow.

Nothing breaks the view; nothing appears to limit it. The whole scene reaches magnificently into space as the road leaves the lake-bed area and climbs toward the steppe plateau which lies between me and the Nevada state line. But its impressiveness gives no feeling of softness and kindliness. It is the desert—monotonous, mysterious, and harsh. One finds few spots which indicate the possibility of shade and moisture. This is the desert of Owyhee. Oregon bounds it on the west, the Snake River on the north, Nevada on the south, and its eastern boundary lies a hundred miles from its western. It is a large county even as Western counties go, containing only three hundred square miles less than the combined area of the states of Connecticut, Delaware, and Rhode Island. One wonders how so much land can look so barren. Stunted junipers grow in scattered clumps in some sections but there is little of softness to relieve the scenery. Flowering plants spring up early in the season, hastening to produce seed which may lie for years before the time is favorable for germination.

The population is as limited as the vegetation is sparse. The 1950 census lists 6,307 in the Owyhee County of 7,648 square miles. Of this number approximately 30 per cent reside in small towns. The county residents, therefore, are rather thinly distributed, about one person to one and three-quarter miles. Murphy, the county seat, has a population of less than one hundred which, of course, includes the county officials. These figures indicate that there can be no feeling of being hemmed in on the part of the inhabitants.

Though a desert area, Owyhee County has been the scene of much activity. Few regions have been so fervently cursed by the first visitors. Its early history matches the harshness of its physical characteristics. Wagon trains traversed it; fur companies exploited it; miners found precious minerals in quantity. But people made no easy bargains with the Owyhee area. The tales of the fur traders record the lack of grass and a shortage of game which forced them to live on the carcasses of the beaver whose fur they sought. Travelers found the mountain passes difficult and rocky. Freighters tested the Snake as a possible means of transportation. The river, unnavigable in spots, crushed the frail boats and, after strewing their contents on the waters, often drowned the rivermen. The word Owyhee was given to the district because three Sandwich Islanders, employed by the Hudson's Bay Company as expert boatmen, were killed by the natives. The name Owyhee is said to be a corruption of Hawaii, the island from which the men came.

The thieving Snake and Bannock Indians became actively hostile. They harried the wagon trains and cut off stragglers. They killed the cattle of the immigrants. They slipped into encampments and drove off the horses. They preyed on freighting parties headed for the mines. They lay in wait for trappers returning with their season's catch and they took not only their furs but their horses, guns, ammunition, and sometimes their clothes as well. The crimes were not all perpetrated by Indians; white desperadoes held up the stages and robbed men who had accumulated a stake at the mines.

Nothing deterred newcomers; during much of the nineteenth century this desert area was constantly visited by immigrants, miners, explorers, fur trappers, and adventurers. Idaho became part of the battleground of the great competing fur companies.

The names of traders and trappers regularly appeared in the records of the period. Pack outfits carried the fur to St. Louis and other markets. The mines brought in eager fortune hunters and filled the hills with mining camps, some of which reached a population of several thousand. They are now ghost towns whose buildings are fast crumbling.

The population of these districts and the activity of the fur traders decreased with the exhaustion of the mineral and animal resources of Owyhee County. Now, only a fraction remains. The country has lost its importance as a fur producer and the mines have shut down. In the meantime, perhaps 90 per cent of this desert area has gone along with little change. Stock grazes the forage areas almost to their production limits (many experts say to more than their limits) . A few strip oases support hay and stock ranches which are mostly the basing points for extensive range operations. Holdings among the large operators are figured in square miles, not sections. The little-traveled roads are much as they were a century ago —the soil undisturbed by the plow, the hills unfrequented by settlers and visited only by range riders. The wild animals build their burrows in the selfsame areas or roam the hills in search of prey, carrying on their daily life as they did many centuries ago.

Owyhee, originally considered and dreaded as a desert, is still a desert, a region of deficient rainfall. Lest my frequent mention of water holes, springs, and strip oases give the impression that water is not really scarce, I give the following revealing figures. Of the slightly more than 5,000,000 acres in the county, the *Economic Survey of Idaho* lists only 57,608 acres as irrigated; the remainder is waste or good only for range. And if the descriptions of summer thunderstorms make it look as if they contribute much moisture, it must be realized that their violence is extremely short-lived and their occurrence scattered and ordinarily confined to the mountains so that almost no rain reaches the desert below—a fact confirmed by the annual precipitation which is only eight to ten inches.

I visited the area primarily to study the activity of the wildlife. How has it adapted itself to existence in such apparently precarious and inhospitable conditions? How does it satisfy its need for food and shelter in a district of light rainfall and temperature ranges from 120° to −35° Fahrenheit? What special adaptations are required?

I have spent much time in observing the life of the natural associations of plants and animals. I observed that each form solves its problems in its own manner. Each species prefers and requires its own type of living. Some animals live in the air, some on the ground. Some burrow beneath the soil surface. Some are carnivores, some are vegetarians. All belong in the desert and possess habits and structures which enable them to stay there.

This book is based on actual field experiences and could have been written in journal form, but that method makes it difficult both to assemble material of a like nature and to emphasize its important phases. Also, I did not wish merely to catalogue desert facts. Instead, I wanted to record impressions of a northern desert as a whole. Accordingly, I have adopted the narrative form so that the characters I have introduced may express the various viewpoints of an ecologist with years of field experience, an assistant who has just finished his education and has returned to the West where he was raised, and an adventurer in conservation, the narrator.

OWYHEE:
THE LIFE OF A NORTHERN DESERT

Spring on the Desert

Perhaps we should begin our story with a description of one of those hot periods which have provided so much material for literature, the drama, and particularly the movies. That is the desert as most people think of it. But there is a time of year when the desert is as gracious and lovely as a fine lady; when moisture is so plentiful that it gives false promise of lasting through the year; when the water holes are clear and full, and the creeks fill the beds which later become so dry. It is the time when tiny plants sprout and bloom and the small mammals romp and mate. We want to put the best side foremost and so we have chosen to begin with spring.

To those who think that this season is so far removed from typical conditions that it is of little interest, we answer that were this season omitted there would be no desert cycle, no preparation of plants for the droughts ahead, no continuance of the desert population, and, from an economic standpoint, it would mean the elimination of the desert as a stock range.

Spring is not only an important but a pleasing season. We always visit the desert with interest, but spring is really the only time when we see it with complete contentment. The roads are solid, possibly on the muddy side in a very few places; the long ribbons of dust, so often mentioned, are lacking. Our viewpoint is one of relaxation. We can work through the day and be comfortable. The ground squirrels and other desert denizens appear as relaxed as we; they display the carelessness which desert dwellers usually show in the early weeks after their emergence in spring. Most of them have already bred and soon we will see young about, feeding with their elders on the plentiful herbage and getting fat as they feed.

We have been asked whether it is best to walk or drive when viewing the desert. Walking provides the intimate view but driving involves a great saving in time when getting to the place where the intimate view is desired—and such places may be many miles apart in Owyhee County.

What do we find at the spring season? Suppose we take a short trip and see what lies south of the Snake River. We leave in the station wagon, the three of us in the front seat, with glasses and notebooks at our sides. We cross the desert lake-bed country, rough, white, and almost bare. The freshness of the air entirely offsets any sense of oppressiveness which is so common during the heat of a summer day. It is as if winter had washed and purified the atmosphere. The sky is filled with great white clouds which move quickly across the clear blue of the background. In summer the mountain outlines fade in the dusty haze, but now everything stands out clearly; the roads do not lose themselves in dimness but show distinctly for miles, until a turn or the passing of a crest blots them from sight.

The vegetation lacks the worn appearance of summer. It does not make us wonder whether the plants can continue to get sufficient moisture to carry them through the season. The gray sagebrush wears little tips of yellowish green. The space under them and close to the rough trunks is occupied by the dried remnants of small plants which have grown and bloomed and scattered seed. They will grow and mature again another year if the sheep do not manage to reach the young plants. The open ground is spotted with the tiny leaves of emerging growth. If plants could hurry, these would do so for they are on a time schedule which necessitates their growth, blooming, and seed setting in a very short time. Shrubs wear spring attire, and some put forth such a profusion of gaily colored leaves that they seem flower-covered.

Spring conditions in the lake-bed area contrast greatly with the bareness of summer. The desert primrose, extremely abundant and perhaps the most characteristic plant of spring, whitens acres with a bloom that appears as fragile as a hothouse exotic. Yellow or red flowers cover the thyme-leaved buckwheat, and narrow-leaved Phacelia blooms in color which varies from bright blue to nearly white. Lupines and many species of astragalus add to the display. Reds, blues, yellows, and whites are present—all the colors which signify spring. As we drive slowly along, we get glimpses of these sprightly spring desert dwellers. The sight always moves me. I recall Wordsworth's description of "Daffodils":

> A poet could not but be gay,
> In such a jocund company!

In the higher altitude of the plateau the vegetation is not as far advanced as in the lake beds. But there will be primrose and tansy mustard blooming. Here and there we will see the flowers of the tall, yellow Cleome, bright and conspicuous among the desert shrubs. Matted Cryptantha, gray and bristly, will hug the ground, as its name suggests—its flowers are small so that its brightness will be appreciated only if we stop. And there the gray ball sage—the purple sage of the Western writers—grows on gravelly slopes. We see sheets of cheat grass—miles of it moving in the morning breeze and rising and falling like the long swells stirred by a distant boat. So many shrubs and herbs bloom that the air is full of the odor, as well as the sight, of spring.

That is why we say there is no sense of lack at this time of year. There is moisture, room, proper weather conditions for all. The vegetation prospers. The usually harsh desert is soft and yielding now. It is gentle like the springs which visit more temperate areas. The cold wind from the snow-covered mountains occasionally chills the air as if to warn that the desert must not be taken too lightly. But even then we have only to find a little shelter and the sun will warm us quickly.

The animal life appears to sense this plenty. For a very short time feed is easy to find. Sheep and cattle browse contentedly, moving slowly, covering little ground during the day and finding much sustenance in the process. Shallow ponds still occupy some of the hollows and water has not stopped run-

ning in washes which are usually dry. A rider passes occasionally, his coat tied to his saddle and his sleeves rolled up. He will pull them down and keep them pulled down in a few weeks, for the desert sun is hard on bare skin.

Overhead the hawks soar back and forth. Their food is plentiful, too, for the small-mammal population is out and around during the breeding and family-raising season. The flying masters of the air feed often and without difficulty. Later on the bountiful spread will have vanished when most of the small animals have sought their burrows and become dormant. But now the ground squirrels dash back and forth in the close vicinity of their holes, gathering the green and succulent food and gorging themselves for the long sleep they will take when drought comes to the land.

The small birds flit about and sing while they choose mates and hunt for nesting sites, which are not always plentiful. Many a fight occurs before the strongest takes possession.

Every person in the desert enjoys the spring: the sheepman because it is the time of increase and shearing; the cattleman because the calves appear and also the grass with which to feed his stock; the occasional travelers because they get the long views and the comfortable temperatures; the road maintainers because the soil is damp enough to be free from dust and will stay where it is put.

It is a lovely, gentle desert then, with all forms of life prospering and finding abundance. But deserts are such that this peaceable condition is only temporary. Spring is but a passing phase which heat and drouth will soon displace. If summer showers come, they will not come regularly; the annual rainfall may be delivered in two or three big storms whose moisture will race down the hardened slopes and leave the ground in almost as parched a condition as before. The passing of spring will end the season of live and let live, and will usher in a time of pitiless competition in which the well-established will crowd out the less well-established; when the strong will displace the weak, and only the especially adapted can survive in the life struggle. There can be little but harshness when the parched, dusty plains lie beneath the withering heat of July and August.

CHAPTER II

Wyomin'

Doc and I occupied the front seat of the station wagon as we drove south toward Owyhee. I sat with pencil and notebook in my hand while Doc expertly handled the station wagon and the trailer which carried our equipment and supplies. It had been nearly sixty days since we had made our spring trip over this same route. Then we had passed through green freshness. Today we would see the results of heat.

Wyomin' napped in the back seat. His final examinations at Wisconsin had kept him more than busy. The trip out West had been economical, but a day coach is not the ideal method of traveling. He gave no sign of waking as we passed through the irrigated strip which so beautifully greened the once desert area around town. The echoes of the car engine against the girders of the Snake River bridge did not rouse him, and we had passed through Murphy, which can be reckoned as one of the smallest of our nation's county seats, without hearing his usually active voice.

I looked back to see how he was faring. "He looks

more like a sleeping child than a young scientist who has just graduated from an Eastern college," I said.

Doc took a quick glance. "He reminds me more of a farm cat or dog in the way he is curled up," he said. "I never saw another nearly six-footer who can relax the way he does. I noticed it when he was in college in Seattle before he went East. He must have learned it from the animals on his father's ranch; when he sleeps, nothing bothers him."

Doc was right. Wyomin' swayed with the motion of the car as if he had been a sack of grain chaff which yielded without resistance. He had made himself comfortable. His gray Stetson was off, his blue shirt open at the top, and his arms limp; his long legs stretched nearly across the car floor. I could see that he had loosened the laces of his new tan work shoes.

Doc continued what he called his "regular observation speed." Thirty-five miles per hour, he contended, got him over the ground plenty fast enough, but not so rapidly that he could not watch the country through which he was traveling. Except on long trips, you could read the speedometer and find it almost exactly at that figure.

The breeze from the west blew lightly, but it was strong enough to distribute thoroughly the dust which the car disturbed. The usual hawks, Swainson's, red-tailed, and rough-legged, soared above us in their search for prey. When I touched the outside of the car it felt as hot as a coal stove. The graveled road was just bumpy enough so that the trailer lurched and pulled at the drawbar. The car had none of the lightness it showed when free of the trailer. When it struck an uneven stretch, it jolted until it finally awoke Wyomin'.

He said nothing for a moment as he gazed out the window, then remarked, "Eohippus! We're out in the desert already. I must have slept an hour."

"How do you like it?" asked Doc. "It's your first look at an Idaho desert and your first entry into Owyhee County."

"It's just about like the one south of Dad's ranch in Wyomin'. All deserts and all Chinamen look so much alike they're hard to tell apart. Deserts are deserts. They all have the same kind of central heating systems. They've got mountains sticking up here and there like corn kernels in pancakes. I can count six rock piles that are probably mountains when you get closer. They look misty and heat-hid just like they do in Wyomin'. Travelin' along you get the feelin' it's not going to end; there'll be another rise just beyond this one, and another one beyond that, and each one will be a little dryer than the one you passed. It's desert, or I was raised in Boston. One thing's certain: it's no stockman's paradise. You understand this is home-folk talk and not a scientific observation on the nature of deserts."

I thought, "He talks just as he did when we knew him as a Freshman in the university at Seattle. He's like a Scotchman, years of experience and contacts won't pry him from his mannerisms and his mountain talk."

We continued as the breeze dropped a little so that the dust drifted over the road in a roll which reminded me of steamer smoke hanging close to the water on a still, heavy day. We came to a series of undulations. Commonly called dips, they followed the contours of dry washes which met the road at right angles. The dips in the road allowed free passage of the flash floods caused by sudden storms. Traveling through these dips provided a roller-coaster effect. Up and down we went, sometimes in a gentle drop of two or three feet and often into eight- or ten-foot depressions which showed how heavily the floods had eroded that particular spot.

"Dips," said Wyomin'. "Sometimes I think they're built like the country where you find them." The car rose to the top of one as a boat rises on the crest of a wave so that the whole surroundings were visible. Then it descended into the next, where only the sides of the depressions could be seen.

"I don't understand your comparison," said Doc.

"Maybe there's a better one. What I meant was this: these dips don't cause any trouble provided everythin' goes all right. They ride smooth and you don't think of them on a day like this. But just let a cloudburst start when you want to get through. It's common as pig tracks to get stalled in one, and maybe get your engine flooded. Or you may have to sit on a high spot because the water in the dips is deeper than you care to chance. I say this whole country's just like that: slick if everything goes all right; but if you run out of water for your engine, or two tires go flat so you are short a spare, or if your battery goes dead—you can be in a bad pickle."

"Sounds reasonable," said Doc. "We'll try to see those kinds of things don't happen."

This is going to be a good combination, I thought: Doc with his years of teaching and field work, Wyomin' with his practical, Western country experience supplemented by his training at both Western and Eastern colleges.

We saw no fences, but an occasional corral provided loading places for stock. Now and then we passed a small puddle or pond with no apparent reason for being. It was a seepage from some underground source or a leftover from a local storm and would disappear, probably, before we passed the spot again. Occasionally a faint wagon trail led across country to some ranch or watering hole. Twice we saw smoke from a distant source. I wondered if they burned sagebrush anywhere, as the early settlers had to do. It would be hard to get enough for fuel in this section; the shrubs were not true sagebrush but one of the desert plants grouped by residents under that name.

Wyomin' stared out the window silently. When he spoke again he said, "Well, we wanted to get into the desert and we've been talkin' about it for three years. Here we are. Sensible folks might wonder why we did so much wantin'. It's gray and dry as an empty beer bottle that's been out in the sun all day. It's hot." He wiped the sweat off to indicate how hot it really was. "It's blow country here. Look at the sand drifted around the bottom of the brush. Look at the little ribbons across the road. I'll bet there's a band of movin' sand a foot high when the wind starts to blow. I've often wondered how some animals protect their eyes when the blast is hustlin' along."

We were near a dozen fair-sized hills on our right. The swales from their drainage crossed the road and made another series of dips. The road began to wind a little so that the long views were lost behind the curves. We dropped into the deepest dip of the day. When we started to climb again a black, fast-moving

shape of a truck blocked the road as it approached.
The short distance between us narrowed rapidly and
a collision seemed inevitable. I wondered if our expedition was to be over so soon. Doc swung the front
wheels and brought the car up on the shoulder on
his side. The driver of the other car acted as promptly.
Brakes squealed to the accompaniment of the fearful
bawling of two calves in the truck. The trailer lurched
under the sudden strain so that it nearly threw us
off the road. How we missed colliding, I will never
know. We passed in a second and, as we passed, we
answered the cheery "Hi" from the rancher in the
other car and the incident was over.

"That was a close one," said Doc. "I guess I should
have been more on my side. All I could think of
when I saw that fellow coming was scrap iron."

"You were drivin' all right," said Wyomin'. "These
roads are so narrow you'd be fightin' ruts all day
if you didn't keep in the middle. That's an every-
day meetin' in this stock country. You don't see anybody for so long you think you're the only man in
the district. Then you meet up like you just did.
You think you'll be awful careful, but in ten minutes
you're right back in the exact center. Range people
never have head-on collisions. I don't know why, but
they always manage to dodge 'em. You'll have lots
of meetin's like this, but if you don't bring back your
car in good shape this fall I'll bet five to one it will
be for some other reason."

A large hawk, a Swainson's, stooped and flew away
with a ground squirrel it had picked up.

"We ought to use them for collectin'," said Wyomin'. "Like the people in the age of chivalry used
to do. Think of the specimens they could bring in.

And think how soft it would be for the collectors.
It would be 'way ahead of beatin' the brush with a
flour sack full of traps."

"I'm afraid it wouldn't work," said Doc. "You speak
about the number of specimens they could bring in.
But how about the variety? Who could teach a bird
to take the kinds you want? They might bring in
twenty specimens you had plenty of and none of
some other kind you really wanted. Hawks specialize
on certain habitats and consequently the variety of
their catch is limited.

"All right," said Wyomin'. "Some people are always fightin' improvements. We'll start baitin' traps
and forget the hawks. I don't know as I'd care to
haul a truckload of huntin' hawks over the country
anyway. And they might be awful hard on the specimens."

The size of the desert appeared more impressive
because of the inactivity in the area. The car proceeded quietly. The heat effectually blanketed anything but sporadic talk. No animals moved about.
Where was all the life of the region?

We stopped for lunch. Doc, the official cook and
meal provider, got out supplies from the trailer. He
moved quietly, knowing the exact location of every
item and producing it without fuss. Cheese, bread,
a tin of cold meat, cookies, and a can of sliced peaches,
lukewarm but delicious, made the meal. Water came
from the tank in the trailer. The water was warm,
but a few months in the field makes one realize that,
hot or cold, it supplies the needed moisture, and
one must not be particular. We drank from warm
springs and water barrels and canvas water bags without complaint.

I watched the distant mountains as we renewed our driving. How different they were from those of the Pacific slope where Doc and I had wandered so many years. Heavy timber covered the Cascades nearly to the five-thousand-foot level. When you traversed their slopes you never knew what you would find; there could be cirques containing lovely mountain lakes, steep cliffs, or mountain meadows full of the little native orchids which frequent such locations. We had seen lichens growing on fallen logs in such numbers that they seemed like flowering plants in bloom. We could visit the same mountain for weeks and each time run into something new.

But it was different on the desert. Here we could see every outline of the mountain ahead. We could catch glimpses of the road as it climbed to reach the pass. Often the surfaces of the gullies were exposed from the base to the top. We could see bold cliffs, the lines of vegetation which indicated the location of the streams that drained the occasional rains. Great piles of rock stood in one place, scattered vegetation spotted it in another. If concealment was characteristic of a mountain in the Cascade Range, the masses before us were marked by bareness and lack of mystery.

Wyomin' resumed his position in the rear seat. He didn't look too happy and I didn't blame him. He had been living in a country where the climatic extremes were not so disturbing. To adjust himself would require time. He perspired freely. His shirt was wet through. He coughed just a little from the irritation of the dust. But he said nothing until Doc asked, "How are you making it, Wyomin'?"

"Changin' climates is like gettin' hung, Doc. It's

a little tryin' at first. I haven't sweat like this since I worked in the harvest the summer before I went East."

"You're not sick of the place already?"

"Eohippus, no! I'm not kickin'. I'm just ashamed because I'm as soft as custard puddin'. If my dad saw me like this, he'd think my college life had ruined me. I've pitched hay in hotter weather and without sweatin' half as much. Give me ten days and I'll be as dry as a playa lake in August."

"You don't want to make camp yet?"

"I'd be awful vexed if you did. If it's goin' to fry, let it fry. The sooner I get the soft grease out of me the better off I'll be. When I think of the things that used to go on in this country, it makes me plumb disgusted to feel worn out."

"What do you mean by that?" I asked.

"I've been thinkin' of the early visitors in this country. The ones who were plundered by Indians and had their horses run off so they had to walk out. The ones who couldn't find game and nearly starved. The miners who were killed by Indians. Comparin' what those pioneers did with what we are doin' is like comparin' Christopher Columbus with people who cross the ocean in a modern steamship. Immigrants with an ox team spent a week in goin' distances we could travel in less than two hours. Fifty miles from water might mean death to them, but we can make it so easily that it seems no problem at all. That's why I don't feel so proud of the shape I'm in."

Doc said, "We're not worried about you, are we, Frank?"

"I should say not," I replied. "In a week you'll be running rings around both of us. As the youngest and huskiest you'll be expected to lead the hard

trips. Doc will run you a close second and, if my
pencil and notebook don't get too heavy, I'll try to
manage and follow you."

One hour's travel brought us to the spot Doc had
planned for our first camp. Some shrubs and brown
grass had been green a few weeks before. But greens
do not last long on exposed, rocky knolls. Doc had
chosen the site because he knew that it would catch
any night breeze that might come up. It was a dry
camp, and we would have to depend on our trailer
supply of water. We set up our tent and put our
cots inside, then got our equipment ready for our
work next morning. Doc pumped up his two-burner
oilstove and furnished a meal of meat and dehydrated
potatoes, stewed corn, bread, canned pears, and coffee.
The sun went down, big and red, and, as Doc worked
on his notes, Wyomin' and I sat on a rock at the
edge of the knoll and watched the shadows spread
over the miles and miles of desert before us.

Wyomin' said little, but I knew he felt better. He
broke the silence to say, "She's big. When I was back
East, I forgot she was so big." He waved his hand
to include the whole desert. "It makes that Middle
West country look as small as a closet in a big house.
I'm feelin' better now. In fact, I'm feelin' perfect.
This afternoon I kicked for the first and last time.
You'll never hear me grouse again about the weather."

We started to talk when Doc joined us, but our
conversation died as darkness came on and, almost
simultaneously, the thought of sleeping bags came to
us. A final wash in little more than a cup of water,
a shift from boots and khakis to pajamas, and we were
on our cots.

I awoke a little later to pull the bag closer around

me, for it was cool. As I looked out the tent opening I could see the blazing stars that mark the desert
night. A little later I wakened quickly as I felt a
mouse frisk over my face. I think I will always be
startled the first time this happens to me each season,
but after that first shock it is not bad at all. They
are dainty little fellows, these desert mice, and as
clean as anybody can ask. They travel so lightly and
rapidly that their passage is little more disturbing
than brushing against a cobweb on the path. At any
rate, although they may have routed themselves my
way many times, I was not aware of it. When I woke
again, Doc was already off his cot and looking about.
A new day had begun.

CHAPTER III

Cool, Cool Water

"I think," said Wyomin', *"that when a man has too* much of anything he kind of loses its full appreciation. Take mountain trout, for example. You think nothin' makes better eatin'; but live close to 'em and, after a month, you won't walk down to the stream for a mess. Or think of people who study music until they know all the answers; some end up by bein' so choosy they don't enjoy anythin'."

"It sounds logical," said Doc. "I suppose something about Owyhee brought it up?"

"Yes, it did, Doc. I've been tendin' that trap line on the wash near the turn of the road. I looked at it closely today. I could see where the water had cut and eddied. The marks looked as fresh as if it still held a gurglin' stream—but the place was as dry as a Freshman's thesis. I compared it with Eastern stream beds that haven't been without water in the memory of man, and I made up my mind that water's like the things I've mentioned—nobody appreciates it if there's plenty."

Doc went to his specimen case to get a squirrel to compare with one he had taken during the morning. Then he said, "I wouldn't say it was that bad. People value the comforts of water, what a nice hot bath means, how satisfying a cool drink can be."

"That's exactly the point. They just think of water in terms of personal comfort. They like it if it's cold and clean and don't taste of any mineral; they crab if it's warm, or if it's a little hard and soap won't lather well, or if it tastes at certain times of the year. They complain without realizin' that water's one of the most important things on earth and they're lucky to have a good supply."

"Well, what do you have in mind doing about it, Wyomin'?"

"Not much. I just thought that people who don't know the real value of water ought to look at an ordinary desert water hole. It's no beauty spot. It's not a shady nook surrounded by greenery, with a spring of clear water flowing out. You can't sit around and dream in the shade and keep cool. If you get too close, you often sink up to your knees in mud. There's enough mosquitoes to keep you slappin'. The cattle tramp it out and mess it up. The flies hover round and keep up a buzzin'. Maybe, if there's a little mite of alkali in the water, the edges are white and the hoofmarks are baked hard. A good many water holes don't rate much higher than an ordinary pigsty.

"Yet each water hole keeps a big area alive. The animals which use it don't mind the dirt. I don't like it myself, but there's been times when I was glad to get some of that muddy water; it didn't taste too bad and it certainly made me feel all right. But the stock doesn't want anythin' better; the critters stand in the mud and they drink long and steady and, when they finish, they go back on the range and stay away until they are thirsty, say one day for sheep and two for cattle. It's all the water they need, but they need that awful bad."

Wyomin' thought that one of the big differences between town and country lay in the manner they got their water. In the city, a turn of one faucet brought cold water and the turn of another furnished hot. Except for the payment of the monthly bill, there was nothing but the replacement of a washer now and then. Town people were used to the system and considered it almost universal. But Wyomin' thought less than 5 per cent of domestic users in the whole world got their water that way.

Most country people obtain their supply by what might be called individual effort. Lots of country water is delivered through taps, but the care of the windmills or power plants which run the pumps is up to the owner who always faces the possibility of a breakage which will put the plant out of commission. Pipes from springs have to be cleaned frequently. They require protection from freshets and freezing. Deep-well pumps must be pulled and valves replaced. Such simple things as water in the gasoline may stop an engine. Very strong winds play hob with windmills. A ranch water supply depends on constant watchfulness. Wyomin' compared the difference between the two systems to fried chicken: in the city you had the butcher deliver the chicken all cut up and ready for the skillet, but in the country you had to catch the fowl, kill, pick, and draw it, and then cut it up before it could be cooked.

Away from the ranches the problem was even more difficult. When doing some fencing, Wyomin' once had been forced to buy water at two bits a barrel and use it while its flavor grew flatter and its temperature higher. It got dirtier, too. One of his two companions had died from fever which the doctor thought came from the water but, if that was so, Wyomin' didn't know why he and the other boy hadn't been sick and maybe died, too. He had been out all summer when the coolest water he drank was from a water bag. It satisfied him, but he knew a "tap-water user" would swear it was hot and dust-mixed and reeking of hemp taste. Wyomin' had seen times when they washed in just a dash and had cooked with tiny amounts of water so their scanty supply would last for the extra day required to finish the job. He said to Doc, "The way we're traveling now, with a trailer and fifteen-gallon tank, is just tops; but if most people had to save water like we do, they'd think they were bein' persecuted."

Wyomin' stopped at the canvas sack for a drink. "It's hot," he said, "compared with ice water, but I always say nobody knows how good water can taste until they are really thirsty and drink from a barrel, a water bag, or even a sticky water hole that you think is all right even if the stock has riled it up."

The wind was rising. The sun was slipping behind the rim. The contrast made it seem a little chilly. We started for our windbreakers almost simultaneously.

Desert water was still on Wyomin's mind when he returned. "It's hard to believe the annual rainfall around here is ten inches or less."

"It sometimes rains more than one hundred inches annually on Pilchuck in the Cascade Range," said Doc. "It reaches one hundred and sixty inches on the west coast of the state of Washington. You can't do much when it rains that way."

"And, puttin' it another way, you can't make eight inches do much for you either, Doc. They used to say it took about thirty inches to raise good corn, over twenty-four inches for strawberries, around thirty inches for orchards, and about forty inches for vine fruits. Dry farmin', when you summer-fallow and let the land lie idle every other year, requires a minimum of twelve inches. I think these figures, though not recent, still stand. But, even if they are a little off, they tell you why you can't do things with an annual rainfall like Owyhee, and especially when the rain doesn't come regular. Sometimes it's dry during the entire growin' season, and more often the downfall comes in one or two big winter rains. Many a new-comer has wasted time and money tryin' to raise crops in a country where the rainfall was too scanty to do the job."

Water is a great limiting factor on the desert. There are two ways to meet the demand: one is to have an unlimited supply; the other is to cut down the need. Since the desert is admittedly a place of deficient moisture, the first condition is seldom possible. All living things must adapt themselves to conditions as they exist. Man is no exception.

Every move of desert folk emphasizes the importance of water. They store and conserve every drop: in the field by proper tilth, in tanks (this name is also given to natural depressions) suitable for storage, behind dams, and in temporary watering holes where permanent storage is not possible. Today the control of watering places on the range is of great importance. One water hole may be the key to control of many square miles. Lack of such spots may make a piece of range worthless except for a short time in spring. Good range must have suitable watering facilities. Many of these places were important in determining the routes of the first immigrants, for horses and oxen were footsore, loads were heavy, and roads or trails in such bad shape that the distances traveled each day were small. Success in finding these watering places helped to insure a successful trip. Failure to locate them, or lack of precautions to determine the next one, might create serious difficulties.

Wyomin' says that Western ranchers won't stay permanently on land unless water is close at hand. He'd seen desert families live for years in tough situations as regards transportation, windstorms, animal predators, heat, and the like, but he'd never seen one who would live in a place where they had to haul water. That seemed to be the breaking point. The women rebelled, the men resented the labor and time required. They wanted to spend their working hours in some other way than riding tank wagons. That's why, in Owyhee and other desert areas, you will find water, good or bad, in sufficient quantity for domestic use, close to the ranch house. People there hunt some sort of an oasis where they can live and raise their winter supply of forage while the stock ranges on the dryer lands in spring, and in the mountains in summer.

That doesn't mean they aren't careful and saving. They are not particular with what city people call the fine points of water. They don't regard it as just one of the things to make life pleasant, as they might do if they lived in town. Without it they can't farm, raise stock, or even live. Failure to maintain a moisture balance means death to an exposed person. Evaporation goes on at so rapid a rate that it can amount to a quart an hour at noon under extreme desert conditions. Needless to say, constant replacement must take place if the person is to live.

The tenderfoot who sucks lemon drops or puts a small pebble under his tongue to combat thirst ignores these facts when he relies on such methods. Psychologically there may be some relief for a very short time, but psychology has little to do with conditions. The process of drying out is caused by heat and exposure to the sun and to the extreme dryness, none of which are altered by pebbles or lozenges. Any protective measures must recognize the cause.

There's a song about a man dying of thirst and being delirious and thinking of water that's cool. I'll bet the man who is dying from lack of water doesn't care whether the water he might get would be cool, or clean, or good-tasting. All he asks is that it be wet. He'd squeeze mud to get some, or he'd drink blood if he could shoot a rabbit or a sage hen. He'd rip open a cactus if he thought he might find it there. There'd be no water hole too foul for him to tackle. He has to satisfy his need some way and he'd not be particular. Thirsty men have drunk salt water and coal oil and many other liquids.

The simplest way to avoid the drying effects of the desert sun is to avoid exposure when it is hottest. Work can be done early or late in the day. I know of a city water department in one Idaho town whose force starts work at daybreak during the hot months. They quit work about noon. We'll see few residents

of Owyhee with large areas of skin exposed. The
sleeveless shirts and scanty shorts may be suitable for
tourists who can get back in the shade when over-
heated, but they do not meet with favor among men
whose working day is steady. Neither is the heavy
protective clothing system of the African desert in
favor, largely, I think, because it is not adapted to
work. Boots, Levi's, denim shirts, often a neckerchief,
and a large hat complete the costume. Gloves of light
leather are much worn. We have always used colored
glasses, but the eyes of the residents must be better
accustomed to the light for few find them necessary.

Desert mammals, like men, have their problems;
the demand for water constantly exists, evaporation
drains off the intake, and the supply must be aug-
mented. They may be divided into a number of rough
classifications: the large mammals such as the deer,
antelope, wildcat, and cougar, all of which must have
regular access to water; the small predators which
derive enough water from their victims; and animals
such as the ground squirrels, which satisfy their demands largely by eating succulent vegetation. In addition there are some like the kangaroo rats which,
through metabolism, convert the dry seeds which they
eat into the water which they must have.

Various devices or adaptations reduce moisture
needs to a minimum. The striking absence of visible
life at noon indicates that practically all mammals
refuse to expose themselves during the hours of greatest dehydration. In addition the burrowers go deep
enough to avoid much of the surface heat. Temperature readings have brought out the fact that the soil
temperature of the desert drops considerably as the

burrow depth is increased. Most of the burrowers plug the entrances as an additional means of controlling the heat. They thus achieve a result compared to the air conditioning of human dwellings. Many of the small rodents go still further: they practice estivation, or summer dormancy, and thus escape the dry season and the heat of summer. Waste matter discharged from their bodies carries little of the precious moisture and is as dry as lead pellets. Urine is disposed of in highly concentrated form. If there is little moisture available, there are many devices to make this little sufficient.

Birds, because their flying ability permits them to cover greater distances, may not be as closely limited as earth-bound mammals. Some, like the Owyhee bluebirds, fly regularly to near-by sources of moisture. The sage sparrows are said to depend largely on dew and the moisture content in the vegetation they eat. The hawks have a comparatively wide range which may diminish their water problems, which is also assisted by the contents of the animals on which they prey. But in all of them we will find some adjustment to the conditions in which they live.

As Doc has remarked: there is a tremendous difference in a country which has an annual rainfall of eight inches and one where it often exceeds one hundred. Certainly the creatures which populate the two areas do not have the same problems. It is easy to predict the disaster which would be produced by a change of populations. Luckily, such a change is not likely. We can predict that the Pilchuck population, conditioned to the downpours and the dripping vegetation of the mountain, will continue to exist efficiently and comfortably. And, some five hundred miles away, the dry stretches of Owyhee will support an equally efficient and comfortable fauna which exists under extremes of heat and dryness.

CHAPTER IV

Time Changes

We met a modern prospector who was camping on the Jarbidge River. He had been working in the Bruneau Creek Mountains. He didn't look exactly as I fancied he should look. He lacked the burro, pick, and shovel so often seen in illustrations. There was a reason: his system was not that of the early prospector. This man used modern equipment; he parked his large trailer at some convenient trading place and then took week-long trips into the hills with his jeep and camping outfit. The quality of his equipment showed he was prosperous. He talked like an educated man and, with his neat clothes and clean-shaven face, looked the part. His trailer contained a small but complete assay laboratory. Two Geiger counters proved that he left nothing to chance. I got the impression that if valuable mineral was around he would find it. He was well informed. He knew the current prices on all the metals. He talked of mines which had been great producers. I gathered that he was a locator rather than a developer of prospects—the kind of a man who acquires good properties which he could sell to operators. I could detect no interest in the mining and stock phases of the business. He mentioned that as soon as he disposed of one property he went out looking for another and in that way, though not making a huge income, he did quite well.

After he left, Doc said, "He's not like the ancient miner I met in the hills three years ago. He had a claim in the Silver City country for which he had been offered seventy thousand dollars. He turned the offer down cold. He wouldn't take 'chicken feed' for a claim that was worth 'millions.' He was going to wait for the 'right price.' The right price never came. He had the property for thirty years without getting a cent out of it and, when he died, he had been living on an old-age pension for some time."

"He was the old type," said Wyomin'. "Lookin' for the one big deal that would make him and his heirs millionaires. This man is new style; he figures that turnover in minin', like in industry, is the way to make a good livin'."

"It's a good way as long as the country isn't all explored," I remarked. "There's just one hitch. These electronic sounding machines, Geiger counters, and other detecting instruments are being perfected to a point where it's going to be hard to hide anything from them. The old prospector had to guess. The new one can make quick and positive surveys; sometimes he can use a plane. He may run out of unexplored places."

"I guess that won't be too soon," said Wyomin'. "This is a mighty big country and they won't get

everywhere for some time. But the fellow we just met certainly has it all over the old boys and their methods. They had rough rules which usually worked, but sometimes newcomers who didn't know the country found ore where experienced prospectors wouldn't even look."

"You're probably right about the time it will take," I said. "I forgot that there's over eighty thousand square miles in the state. And some of it is mighty rough."

"I should say so," said Doc. "Natural forces have worked Idaho over thoroughly. Conditions go from one extreme to another. It has been raised into mountains and worn down. It has been moist and mucky and inhabited by big prehistoric animals. There have been many periods of volcanic activity. The glacial age put some of the northern parts under ice sheets of tremendous thickness. The streams cut big canyons and made the falls which we've seen in so many places in the state. It took millions of years to do it, but I don't suppose there is a state in the Union that has been more completely modeled and remodeled and that varies so much in different parts."

I had learned the truth of this when I made my first trip from the lake and timber country of the Panhandle in the north, past Lake Coeur d'Alene, through Lewiston on the Snake River, over the fertile Camas Prairie, through the timber district and mills of McCall, and then to Boise, prosperous with its irrigation. Elevations range from seven hundred feet at Lewiston to Mount Borah, which peaks at more than twelve thousand feet.

Climatic conditions in the state vary from those of the desert in Owyhee County to the moisture and cold of the comparatively humid timber-covered sections. We found places where lakes are the principal natural features, and others where any kind of standing or running water of size is a rarity. Timbered hills are as common in the north as bare hills in the south.

Owyhee presents a broken kind of topography. Seven mountain ranges, the Ruby, Silver City, Juniper, South Mountain, White Rock, Elk, and Owyhee Highlands are scattered in an apparently haphazard manner over the country. Between them are more or less level areas, except where they are intersected by the river canyons. Generally speaking, the altitude of these flat areas is lowest at the northern boundary and increases in elevation to the south. The northern area is known as the "lake-bed" desert portion because it is closely associated with ancient Lake Idaho, the size of which is roughly outlined by the exposed lake beds which extend from east of Glenns Ferry west into Oregon and include an area of almost twenty thousand square miles. This tremendous body of water lasted until a break occurred in its northern wall and the water drained out through the present Hell's Canyon of the Snake River.

The lake-bed desert is roughly divided into two parts, the first of which, from 2,200 to 2,500 feet, lies along the Snake River and is composed of more or less unconsolidated sand, silt, and gravel in flood plains, landslides, and dunes. The rest of the lake-bed desert, above 2,500 feet and below 3,300 feet, is mainly what the geologists have called in the past the "Payette Formation," which consists of somewhat more consolidated sand, silt, and gravel from the shores, tributaries, and beds of ancient Lake Idaho. In this latter formation are also sandstones, tuffs, diatomaceous earth, and a little lignite. Thin basalt caps may be seen on some of the erosional buttes and mesas of this formation.

As previously mentioned, this lake-bed desert is the driest of the country. The vegetation is low and sparsely distributed. It supplies meager spring pasture for sheep. Some of the soil is nearly as white as chalk. In places the whiteness is overlaid by dark basalt so the effect might be compared with vanilla ice cream and chocolate sauce. Murphy, the county seat, concentrates its few buildings in a corner of the lower lake-bed district.

Owyhee appears quiet enough now, but every geologist can find many records of past activity. As the old rocks of the district wore down, lake and stream deposits covered the low places and lavas welled up and added their layers. The various layers are still in evidence. Crustal pressures produced uplifts and faultings and mountains again rose to great heights. In the meantime the streams began their destruction so that channels and canyons were deepened. Obstructions had caused the ponding of the river and the creation of ancient Lake Idaho. Into it the streams poured their loads of material and the wind blew volcanic dust until the lake was filled to a depth of approximately a quarter of a mile. Intermittent lava flows further increased the deposits.

At first it was strange to us to see how much of the rock was of sedimentary origin, or laid down in water. How could this desert area ever have been wet enough to permit the laying down of material to the depth of a thousand feet or more? We found sediments in the hills, thrust up by movements of the crust, mixed with the basalts which flowed inter-

mittently, and far from the position they occupied
when they were being formed. Stream action sorted
the silt as it settled, the finer particles traveling farther, the heavier being deposited when the current
slowed down. As the thickness increased, the pressure
forced the materials together into a compact mass,
and some cementing material formed them into rock.

As we leave the lake-bed desert on its south side,
at an elevation of about 3,300 feet, we meet the
escarpment, or steep slope, of the Owyhee Plateau
which lies at a higher level than the lake-bed country. The sediments of the lower country are replaced
by material called the Snake River basalt, but some of
the streams have cut down through this basalt to an
acid volcanic lava called rhyolite. The mountains of
Owyhee, such as War Eagle Peak near Silver City,
are in part granite or grandiorite of the great Idaho
Batholith, or of rhyolite such as is found on Cinnabar
Ridge. There are also some Columbia River basalts
on some of the lower flanks of the Owyhee Mountains.

It may sound a bit complicated to the untrained
reader, but it is like a photograph or a printed record
to a geologist. Briefly and simply, the presence of lava
indicates volcanic activity of some sort. The various
layers of basalt and their different compositions, together with the layers of other materials lying between
the lavas, prove that volcanism occurred in widely
separated periods, the length of which may be more
or less accurately determined by an examination of
the deposits. There is much evidence to show that
water has greatly complicated the original situations
by cutting down through some strata to expose others
and by laying down isolated sediments such as the
alluvial deposits in Duck Valley in the south-central

part of the county. They may find small snowbank cirque remains to prove that mountain glaciers had once been active in small degree in a few of the higher mountain elevations, but it is quite certain that they would find no signs that the great continental ice sheet had come that far south in the state.

Volcanic activity has been great in Idaho. We are concerned particularly with the Snake River lava flow which is said to be among the greatest known in the world. It began in early time; it occurred through the ages; there are many records of activity within historic times. There appears to be no reason why such activity should not occur again.

The finding of fossils presents other information about early conditions. These evidences of ancient life have been widely found in the county. From a study of these fossils the experts have established that ancient horses, mammoths, elephants, and mastodons once lived in the area. They have found fossils of clams, gastropods, and shells. Fish bones and the jaws of drum fish have been uncovered.

That the area was not always desert is shown by the fossils of the leaves of such broad-leaved trees as oak, maple, elm, alder, sassafras, willow, and others. Fossils of conifers are also plentiful. The finding of fossil bones of camels, bison, beaver, musk ox, and bear not far from the county indicates that such discoveries may be duplicated sooner or later in Owyhee.

The average traveler has little opportunity to view fossils but few can fail to see what the geologists call erosion remnants, those strange and fantastic forms which have been carved by water and wind during the centuries. Just across the Snake River and over the county line near Marsing is Lizard Butte, which is said to be a remnant of a volcanic vent. It is a most remarkable likeness which can be spotted instantly by a passer-by. Its legs, head, body, and tail are clearly defined as it lies sprawling in the attitude so often taken by living lizards.

In other areas the natural erosive agencies of snow, ice, wind, and stream have done their work. Unequal erosion has left queer remains so grouped that they have been called "cities of rocks." They stand in remote places which, from a distance and in the uncertain light of dawn or dusk, might be mistaken easily for a sleeping village with extinguished lights and fires. No such extensive clusters are reported in Owyhee limits, but they are close. But one cannot ride a day without seeing eroded remains which one fancies resemble men, or cats, or other mammals. Near the head of Castle Creek we found a row of statuesque "hoodoos" standing quiet and solemn on the side hill. They were the erosional remnants of a dike composed of rock harder than the surrounding material.

Time changes in Owyhee as elsewhere. The rocks drop as we pass cliffs; the winds keep the scouring sand in motion. The climate has changed and will probably change again.

CHAPTER V

Tommy, the Sand Hog

I thought, as I walked along behind Wyomin' on broken ground, if ever a man looked as if he came from and belonged to the soil it was the one I followed. He wore khakis that day, his hat was of the color and type of Doc's, and they looked much alike when at rest, but there was something about him when he moved that placed him as a "loose ground" man whose early gait had been adjusted to irregular surfaces and deep furrows. There was no apparent attention to the rough terrain beneath but, just the same, there was an accommodation which resulted in a perfectly smooth and effortless progress.

Another thought came to me one morning as we sweated in a tiresome climb to a summit. The sun had warmed us uncomfortably. Why was I here? Why was I enduring the annoyance of such conditions and, above all, why did Wyomin', who could have been a well-paid and welcome assistant on his father's ranch, choose to follow a vocation in which discomforts were

almost the rule? Why had he gone to college and
then taken his master's degree in the East? Why did
people voluntarily make such choices?

I toiled up the ridge while I thought. A projecting
rock just rubbed my ankle, but its sharpness scratched
like a knife. It was the result of carelessness which
Wyomin' would have escaped. He never banged his
fingers or skinned his elbows. He was an outdoor
precisionist; he was a born rancher and yet he had
gone into scientific work. How had a country boy
been attracted to biology so strongly that he followed
it? In college, few students had any definite goal.
The fellow who knew just where he was going was
considered a lucky chap. I wondered if Wyomin' was
in that class or if his choice had been purely accidental. The idea which would have avoided all this
speculation came to me: why not ask him?

"Wyomin'," I said, "how did you happen to go into
biology as a profession? I never heard you say. Did
some older man suggest it?"

"No, it was a natural thing. My curiosity got me
to investigatin' all the animals I saw around the ranch.
There was always somethin' new; rabbits came and
went in droves, horned owls would stay away from
the place for years, then they would start heavy raids
on chickens. Chipmunks and ground squirrels would
be everywhere in spring and early summer; then they
would disappear. I wondered why. Maybe, if somebody could have told me all about it, I would have
been satisfied, but the puzzle got greater and I just
had to know. I kept watching and learned a lot while
I hunted, but it was only the surface things I found
out about. I couldn't get the answers that interested
me. Why didn't all animals have about the same

habits? Why did some stay around all winter, and others go in early fall? I asked my dad but he didn't know."

"Did it bother him to have you wasting your time that way?"

"No, he thought it was just a kid's foolishness. I always did my chores first, if I do say so. So he wasn't bothered."

"Well, how did you actually get in further?" I asked.

"In high school we had a science teacher who noticed my interest and asked me how I was goin' about my study. I told him I just looked at whatever I happened to see. He suggested that I specialize on one species at a time. He thought concentration would tell me a lot more about the one animal and a lot more, too, about all others. That's what got me really interested. He said I'd learn to think, and analyze and draw conclusions; and I did."

"You selected some animal?"

"No, I just happened to run across one. Vacation began the following week and I took some cattle into the hills where the snow had just gone off. In a little swale I saw some long, round objects that were smaller than fire hose and appeared to be old rotten rolls of something. They were dirt and they lay all over the hollow. Some of them entered the ground; others left one common spot and ran out a few yards and stopped. I figured an animal had made them, but I couldn't see why or how. Why would an animal shape dirt into the form of a forty-foot sausage? And if an animal did do it, how did he go into the ground? I made up my mind I was goin' to find out and I did.

"I was lookin' after some of Dad's stock in the area for the bigger part of the summer. Whenever I wasn't

busy, I would go around lookin', but I never saw an animal until early one mornin'. I left my horse on the other side of the swale and then sneaked behind a rock where I could hide and see without bein' seen. The risin' sun had begun to heat the pocket when I saw a movin' pile of dirt near one of the holes in the swale floor. The pile moved forward and behind it came a brown animal of a little bigger than mole size. It used its breast as a plow and swept the dirt clear of the hole and to one side. Next, it moved back until its haunches were inside the hole. Then it began to nibble leaves from a small bush just above.

"I didn't get the long look that I expected. A golden eagle was hoverin' above. I guess it saw the animal move but it didn't see me behind the boulder. It dropped like a rotten rock from a cliff. The animal had about as much show as a turkey at a Thanksgivin' Day shoot. The shadow of the divin' bird just happened to pass across the burrow entrance. A movin' shadow in such a place is like a fire alarm siren—it's a powerful warnin'. All hunted creatures must sense that it's death to neglect it. The bird was almost there, but the hindquarters of the animal got busy and snapped him back into the hole as if he had been grabbed by a feeder on a hay baler. No meal for that bird, and was he mad—you could have heard him a mile.

"I got a book on animals by mail from the state and I read it halfway through before I found the animal was a pocket gopher, called that because it had pouches on either side of its face to carry things in. Its scientific name was *Thomomys* and I wanted to be scientific, but it was too much for me and so I just called him Tommy for short.

"I discovered a lot by observation, and some of the things I thought I found out were wrong. For instance, I saw workings all over the swale so I figured there must be dozens of pocket gophers to build so many nestin' burrows. Then I read the animal hunted in underground runways like a mole, except the gophers ate roots and the moles concentrated on insects, worms, and other animal life. A gopher would build runways as fast as it wanted to reach new food; its tunnels were everywhere.

"I tried to find out about them from different ranchers but, although some had seen those ropes and wondered a little about them, they didn't bother enough to find out. Some of them had never seen a pocket gopher. They didn't know too much about their habits or their looks. They probably laid most crop damage to jacks, which got so plentiful every few years."

"What interested you so much about them?" I asked.

"They kind of mystified me. I saw those funny ropes but noticed that I only found them in the higher snow country. I saw their workin's so often I came to recognize them. They were everywhere, just like they are in Owyhee County, but the animals themselves hardly ever showed up. Once in a while I'd see one on a cloudy day or late evenin'. They had different habits from the ground squirrels and chipmunks. I knew that ground squirrels went into estivation or summer sleep when it got dry and the feed got scarce, but I saw signs that the pocket gophers didn't estivate or hibernate, for I ran across fresh workin's every month in the year.

"Partly by observation and partly by readin', I got a lot of the answers. Tommy was a tunnel builder and a

specialist in it. He was like the men they called sand
hogs who came into the state and built irrigation and
railroad tunnels. I started callin' him Tommy, the
Sand Hog. But, unlike human sand hogs, who spend
less than one third of their time makin' tunnels and
the rest of their time livin' and restin' and amusin'
themselves above ground, Tommy lives in his tunnels
and is probably absent from them less than 1 per cent
of his life.

"You know a lot about the pocket gopher, Frank,
but I am tellin' you the whole story of my experience
with it. I found that underground passages weren't
just a sideline with Tommy. He lives in them, he
raises his family in them, and he secures the bulk of
his food, roots, and bulbs by tunnelin'. He doesn't
like bein' above ground. Maybe he feels secure only
when he has soil all around him. He'd rather tunnel
thirty feet than walk across the ground above the run-
way. He's afraid of the outside, I guess, and it's
uncertain territory for him, so he's content to stay in
the darkness.

"That's the kind of a mammal that I'd picked for
my first investigation; one that never got above ground
where you could see him, and who traveled through
his workin's when he wasn't sleepin'. His specialty
is darkness, and tunnelin.'

"When I say Tommy is a specialist, it means a lot
more than to say that about a man. Human specialists look about the same as other men. You can't tell
by lookin' at a man on the street whether he follows some specialty and, if he does, what particular
one he works at. A specialist among men does his
work with certain tools and equipment. If a man
is a sand hog, he uses such devices as metal shields,

compressors, jackhammers, and excavatin' machines to do the job.

"But I guess very few animals, except men, rely on or can use any kind of equipment to make their work easier. Tommy certainly doesn't. He has to rely on his own physical structure, or what you might call built-in equipment, to perform his specialized jobs.

"He has this built-in equipment, all right. He hasn't got such things as the long legs of a jack rabbit, for road speed wouldn't do a tunneler a bit of good. He doesn't have the keen eyes of a hawk, for how could they help an animal livin' in darkness, dim twilight, or small twisty tunnels?

"He does have what it takes to fit him to win, hands down, the free-style burrowin' contest for animals under fourteen inches in length. His eyes are small but he has sensitive whiskers (they call them *vibrissae*) and an almost hairless tail full of nerves. It's a slick combination and better than eyes; it's really radar ahead and astern so he can travel at high speed in either direction almost as well.

"I never saw him tunnel. I have to take the word of those who have kept pocket gophers under conditions where they can be observed. They do a job with top efficiency. Two sets of big incisor teeth set at the proper angle take the place of jackhammers and diggin' spades. The mouth is a slit protected by fur to keep the dirt out. Diggin' is done with it entirely closed, although the big diggin' teeth are uncovered. Human sand hogs use a tunnel muckin' machine to remove the loose material. Tommy has a system of his own—his strongly muscled forelegs, endin' in long curved claws, aid the diggin' and clear the loosened dirt by passin' it under the animal and to

the rear. The claws can be bent under the feet when
not in use.

"Tommy doesn't remove the material from the tunnel, as many think, by fillin' his cheek pouches. They
are used to carry food. When he gets a pay load,
he turns around (he is close-coupled so that he can
turn in almost any passage) and pushes the debris
to the tunnel entrance. That's where I saw him for
the first time."

"You've made a study of the pocket gopher," I
observed. "How long did it take you?"

"Ever since I was in high school. I never pass a
pocket gopher site without lookin' it over. I checked
one yesterday when I was over at the pass. I always
stop. Sometimes I learn something new.

"His build makes him a clumsy waddler above
ground, but it helps him below. His thick skull,
powerful chest muscles, short, heavy neck, and blunt
front give him the equipment necessary so he can
easy build rods of interlockin' tunnels.

"I've done enough diggin' around to learn a lot
about his way of livin' and I've read what others have
found out. His home consists of more than one burrow tunnel. His underground passages include tunnels for storage, for livin' quarters for the young, and
for travel and huntin'. He leaves openin's to the
surface, plugged when not in use, for dirt disposal.
He fills old passages which have served their purpose
with dirt from the new workin's. I've often wondered
how much time is spent on new tunnelin' and in the
maintenance of old ones.

"There was still snow when I finally saw for myself how Tommy built those ropes. He seems to like
snow at times, I guess because he can tunnel through

it at levels which let him reach vegetation he can't
get at from the ground. Instead of a sand hog, he
is a snow hog then, and he starts buildin' networks
in the easily penetrated snow. He uses some of these
workin's for travel; others he packs with waste dirt
from below. The results are what fool people; these
long dirt rolls keep their shape even after the snow
melts. When I saw them they were in all stages—
those in the shade where the snow hadn't melted were
still above ground; but, in the sun, the disappearin'
snow had let them down so they laid wet and ragged
on the bare dirt—long soil ropes which start many
a man guessin'.

"I've dug into their workin's and found their nestin'
chambers and once I found three young. I located
storage compartments with short pieces of roots in
them. I would like to have had more time for watchin'
them and diggin' around, but I had to keep workin'.
I met one field man who told me a lot about them.
I think most of what he knew came from watchin'
captive animals. They are almost silent, solitary and
ill-natured, unwillin' to get along with each other
except the opposite sex in breedin' season. Efforts to
cage them together usually result in a fight and the
death of one of them.

"The meanness isn't confined to captives. Their burrows are said to be plugged against each other so
that what might be intended as a neighborhood call
ends up as a pitched battle. The fact has been used
to catch one by lowerin' another roped gopher into
the burrow and withdrawin' the two when they begin
to clinch.

"Tommy, the sand hog, has his points. One of them
could be copied by human sand hogs. He is said to

go a lifetime, if necessary, without taking a drink. Even if he does occasionally burrow in irrigation ditches, he does some good by general workin' over of the soil and improvin' its quality. He manages to hold his own in spite of his enemies and is found over much of the Northwest and in wide extremes of temperature and moisture.

"He has many enemies. Hawks and owls visit his burrow areas and there is no doubt that they often take an animal which gets a yard or two from its entrance. Foxes, coyotes, and badgers try to dig them out. Ferrets and weasels enter the tunnels. If Tommy invades tilled fields and is recognized by man he will be hunted with dogs, guns, and poison.

"And man has reason to hunt him. Modern research has placed him as one of the top mammal enemies of agriculture. Experts estimate that his annual damage exceeds ten million dollars. Roots, bulbs, grains, shrubs, and orchards are attacked. He evades many attempts at control.

"That's what I learned about one mammal when I took my high-school teacher's advice and started to specialize. When I got through I was so interested I figured I wanted to keep up that kind of work."

"You don't seem to think much of Tommy," I said.

"Then you've got me wrong. Economically, he can be awful tough on agriculture. Regardless of economics, which place him as an enemy in one place and a friend under other conditions, Tommy is an interestin' example of extreme specialization in nature. We have to get rid of him when he competes with agriculture, but there may be some locations right in Owyhee where he can continue to build his tunnels and live his life without botherin' man."

CHAPTER VI

Desert Storm

We looked at the water rushing through the wash which had been dry when we crossed it less than six hours before. Now it was nearly four feet deep and dark with the load of silt which it carried. The main storm was over but scattered raindrops, hurled by the wind, splashed against the windshield of the station wagon. Low clouds still covered the sky, medium gray above us but black and menacing in the direction the storm had taken.

"Eohippus, but that's certainly a waste," said Wyomin'.

"What's a waste?"

"That water rushin' by, Doc. If it could be spread out over the land, think of the good it would do. The desert not only gets little rain but what it does get usually falls like this."

We could look farther up and see the brown thread of water as it moved down the slope in the wash.

"It's nearly bankfull," said Doc. "It will probably

hold up that way for half an hour. We'd better get out the grub and eat. The storm has passed but driving will be better if we wait." He opened the canvas on one corner of the trailer and got out supplies.

"We can't kick about being delayed," I said. "It's our own fault that we're here, but it has been a good show and worth it."

It certainly had been our own doing. We had passed this spot earlier in the day on our way south. We had stopped a few miles beyond to do some field work. A tremendous cloud had begun to build up in the district to the west. It was white at first. Slowly it increased in height and lateral extent. Its underside took on a black color and an "anvil" formed on top, plain warning that a large active storm was ready to break. It moved just to the south of us, growing darker and darker. Numerous flashes of lightning dropped out of it, and soon we could hear the distant rolls of thunder which became louder and louder. Streaks of rain, not reaching the ground and known as "virga," appeared. Soon these grew larger, and eventually a solid black column of water descended from the sky to the ground—a cloudburst. It was coming closer. Squirrels and chipmunks had disappeared, no birds sang, and the desert around us became very still.

"It's goin' to be a golldinger," said Wyomin'. "It will cross the road about a mile or two from here. I'd like to see what it would be like if we got close to it."

"That's just my idea, too," said Doc. "What do you say, Frank? Shall we drive back and tangle with it?"

"The committee is unanimous," I said. "We're here to learn about new and strange things. This will be something new and maybe a little stranger than we like."

"Short of a wind that would pick up the car, we're all right," said Doc. "If we stay inside we're pretty safe from lightning—a car is well insulated, you know. If there's a cloudburst, we may be stranded for a while by a section of washed-out road, but I think it's worth risking."

We battened down the trailer canvases. We jumped into the car when Doc started the engine, and we located our raincoats so we could use them if we had to get out. We tightened the windows to prevent the rain from driving in. The smell of wet sage preceded the storm. Flashes of lightning became more frequent. We noticed flying dust raised by the roll cloud, the low-hanging portion which is ahead of the main cloud. Doc turned on his lights, for it was getting dark. Soon we stopped.

The exact spot he chose stood high enough to clear any flood, but just ahead of us the road made a six- or seven-foot dip and crossed the wash.

The car was facing the storm, which struck us almost immediately. Rain, at first only a few drops, increased rapidly until it became a regular torrent whipped into spray by the heavy gusts. Intermittent gushes reduced the visibility to only a few feet. The water splashed against the car. Claps of thunder mingled with the plop of the driven drops. It was a low, grumbling mixture which appeared to come from everywhere. The hard ground absorbed so little water that almost every foot was covered with small streams seeking an outlet. Then the wash ahead filled with water and became a rush of oily, yellow motion. The air cooled somewhat. The wind shrieked through the juniper and sagebrush, and their overpowering smell filled the air. The shallow ditches alongside the road were filled with water, as were the hollows on either side of our observation point. The spattering of the raindrops raised little columns which were immediately attacked and flattened by the wind.

One flash of lightning succeeded another so that the roar of close thunder was almost continuous. For a short time the storm increased in intensity and then, almost as quickly as it had come, it tapered off and moved away. We could see its blackness and the lightning flashes for some time.

We had said nothing during the storm. Doc broke the silence. "That's what they call a cloudburst. You've seen it all—the puffy-sided cumulus clouds which rise and expand until they can get no higher because they weigh more than the air they try to displace. They flatten out then as this one did and form what they call, because of its shape, an anvil top, which almost always projects in the direction the storm is moving. Below, in front, there is usually a roll cloud which is a dark, dirty gray and is set in rotation by upward currents."

"How high do the tops get?" asked Wyomin'.

"They differ according to the season and the latitude, but the maximum heights I have read about in the Northwest are below thirty thousand feet. As you'd expect, the higher they get, the bigger fuss they kick up."

The rain had almost stopped and so we got out of the car. The ground was soaked and sticky. Four feet of water crossed the wash just below us, running smooth and oily with its weight of sand. Uprooted sagebrush and other vegetation floated by. The mud

prevented us from walking far, so we stood where
the ground was rocky and watched. In a few minutes
more of the road became visible as the stream low-
ered. A foot or two still ran in the dip, and the road
was not in shape for traveling; we did not care to
proceed and drop into a hollow of unknown depth
which might flood our engine. It was then that Doc
proposed we eat. We talked more of thunderstorms
while we ate.

The storm we had passed through was of the
orographic or mountain type and was not at all uncommon during the summer. The great thermal
trough, associated with or in the interior valleys of
California and eastern Oregon, brings up warm, un-
stable air from the southwest coast. This is triggered
into thunderstorms by the mountains in the desert.
The storms seem to hit a cycle which varies from
year to year. The summer of 1953 did not get into
the pattern, and there were very few storms.

Thunderstorms of this type form out of an expanding column of air. As the column rises, moisture
changes from the gaseous state to the liquid. In so
doing, heat is released which is given off to the air
column, causing it to rise further, thus making the
process a self-feeding one. In time the moisture drop-
lets combine to form drops of rain which are supported by strong updrafts of air. As they hit each
other, they break and reform, producing static elec-
tricity which occasionally arcs over to an opposite
charge in another part of the storm, or to the earth
in the form of lightning bolts. The turbulence continues in the clouds. As the drops of water are blown
higher, they reach the freezing zone where they form
hail. After a while they attain a size where the air

will no longer support them and they fall toward the ground. If they are in the downdraft area of the storm, they are actually propelled to the ground by wind pressure in a descending column called a rain gush or cloudburst. The storms usually dissipate after much of their moisture or energy has been used or when, as in the evening, the surrounding air becomes so cool that the warm storm mass is chilled.

"The Owyhee storms," said Doc, "begin over mountains as little puffs of cumulus which grow in size during the morning (when most of them form) into larger masses, expanding fastest in the vertical direction, often forming into great towers in a few hours. Once they get a start, the gradient wind catches them and moves the whole system in the direction the wind is blowing. There are definite trajectories in Owyhee County, and the paths of most thunderstorms can be predicted with a fair degree of accuracy. A single storm seldom lasts over a quarter to half an hour in any one place, although there may be a succession of them lasting from six to eight hours. Winds may be gusty from forty to fifty miles. Well—I see this storm is about over."

The water had nearly subsided in the dip in front of us. We decided to get back on our original course. A considerable amount of silt and sand was deposited on the road, and we learned the next day that several stretches had been badly cut up. We watched a couple of cars as they cautiously passed. We heard later that they had considerable difficulty in getting over some sections that had been recently graded and were still soft. Soon after, we were flagged down by the sheriff, who wanted some detailed road information. He had just come from Big Spring and said that the storm had been very heavy there and about a mile of road was almost ruined. Luckily, we were just on the edge and were driving away from the disturbance and so had little trouble.

"Those storm paths you speak of, Doc," Wyomin' said. "I suppose that the pattern has quite an effect on the county?"

"It certainly has," said Doc. "Not only the precipitation but the cloudiness and winds of such storms affect temperature and evaporation. No doubt the Bruneau Desert is largely what it is today because of its flatness and the fact that it lies too far east of the scarp ranges to receive any value from showers."

The air was extremely clear now and the outlook inspiring. Far to the southeast the Owyhee Plateau swept up to the mass of the Jarbidge Range, gashed in several places with the great cuts of the canyons.

We turned the car and retraced our route toward Poison Creek Pass. The mountain slopes presented a barren, treeless appearance which was broken only by the brush bordering the creek. The air was hot and humid from the passing storm. A bubbling and steaming up front indicated that our heavy load, combined with the atmospheric conditions, was working our radiator to its limit.

Doc turned on the radio to pick up the news. All that a search of the dial revealed was one dance band, two hillbilly singers whom Wyomin' compared to "dyspeptic coyotes," a gloomy commentator, a tin-pan organist, and a whodunit. The last was the usual pat plot about a doddering "fence," two toughs, a Reno sheriff who called his home state "Nevahda," as no Westerner would have done. That was our choice: a story about the West that an Easterner

would have written, unmelodious, supposedly Western songs, a clumsy organist who insisted on sticking
to the shrillest registers, and a commentator who tried
to call the turn on a future which could not be ana-
lyzed. Doc looked at us expectantly.

"Let's get back to thunderstorms," said Wyomin'.
"At least they'll cool a fevered brow."

"I thought I'd talked you out and I wanted to give
you a change. We didn't mention the other kinds of
thunderstorms. I can describe them briefly if you'd
like. There is another type of air-mass thunderstorm
that is quite similar to the orographic storm which
I've described. It's the result of the heating of the
earth's surface which makes a draft and sends an air
current upward. A cumulus cloud forms and the
build-up of the storm begins.

"The third type is the frontal. This is caused by
the moving of a cold-air mass into a place where
the air is warm, or the moving of a warm-air mass
into a place where the air is cold. These meetings of
air masses of unequal temperatures and other physical characteristics cause the warm air to move up
over the colder mass, a proceeding which causes a
lot of disturbance. The first condition is called a cold-
front type and often causes a whole line of thunderstorms, usually at low altitudes. The second type, aris-
ing when warm air moves into a region of cold air,
occurs at much higher altitudes. These frontal storms
come out of general air conditions and are much less
common than the orographic type which rises from the
local conditions usually present in mountain country."

"Well, the storm we had today was certainly a fancy
job," said Wyomin'. "It must have taken a lot of
doin' to get all that energy rampagin' around. It

appears that buildin' up such a storm in dry country would be like pickin' half a dozen rabbits out of a stovepipe hat the way the magicians do."

"I wouldn't exactly O.K. the comparison," said Doc, "but today's type is certainly a job built on local specifications, which are followed by a good many storms a summer. Each day we see cumulus clouds start to form in the morning. The storm doesn't always come off, usually doesn't in fact, but the potential is always there."

"Anyhow, they don't do much harm and they don't do much good," said Wyomin'. "If they were of direct benefit you'd see more green fields. They usually unload right on the mountains themselves, but if they do reach the desert slopes the downfall comes so fast that the land can't absorb it and the washes carry it away like the gutters carry away the rain on a shingle roof. I've seen towns in California that could use such a good system of water disposal."

"When you watch these storms you think that they must do a lot of damage, but there are very few people killed by lightning. Maybe it's because the population is so small and because people take to cover. Once in a while a sheepherder in the high country gets killed out in the open. Of course, that's about the most exposed place a man can get into."

We have had experience with another type of desert storm. On a Friday, while passing through open country where we could watch the cumulus clouds as they boiled and mushroomed into huge shapes, we saw one which didn't look exactly like those we had seen before. This one had a long, tubelike appendage which almost reached the ground. We hopped out and climbed a small hill which overlooked the country.

We could not have found a better observation point. Through our glasses we watched the tube, progressing irregularly and stirring up clouds of dust where it touched the ground. It passed not more than two miles away and was so well outlined that we got good pictures. Other tornadoes had been reported in the state but we had never seen one. The sight reminded me of a huge vacuum cleaner progressing steadily and sucking everything into its path as it progressed. We watched the radio for some report of the damage done, but apparently its path continued in almost unoccupied grazing country for the storm was not even reported.

That, I thought, was the great difference between storms in the city and in our area. In the city, the concentration of people and buildings is great. A storm appears to embrace the whole area and dominate it with its strength. In every severe storm somebody is usually hurt, or a building is destroyed, or a power plant put out of commission temporarily. But when we watch the storms in a western-range area like Owyhee, they appear to attack but a small part of the country. The wind may come and lightning may fill the air ahead of us, but if we look to the side or behind us, we may see the sun shining in the distance. If the lightning strikes, it is usually on some high ridge or sharp peak. In the valleys and canyons below, the rancher and his family stay in safe shelter.

CHAPTER VII

Going Places

Going places on the Owyhee Desert is not always simple. You can't start driving and figure on taking your pick of half a dozen motels in the town you reach about 4:00 P.M. There just aren't any towns with such accommodations. You are badly fooled if you think you can pick up a tasty luncheon snack in one of the drive-ins which must line the road. You won't find any. If you think the few gallons of gas in your tank can be replaced whenever you run out you may meet up with a big surprise. Empty tanks are most embarrassing. Of course, the one and only main north and south road between Idaho and Nevada will have most of these facilities, but on the others you had better adopt the Boy Scout motto and "be prepared," for on the desert you approach the primitive in transportation. If you intend to do anything but drive straight through, you must have camp equipment, plenty of gasoline, and a water supply. You may not need it, but an emergency supply can be extremely valuable.

Idaho is a progressive state and the people in its counties are progressive. But it must be understood that roads are a real problem. Owyhee, as previously stated, has a total population of less than 6,500. The area of the county exceeds 7,600 square miles. These few people are spread all over the county. It takes some doing to keep them all in touch with the railroads and the markets. Roads must not cost more than people can afford to pay. As compared with Eastern conditions, consider one of the towns of six or seven thousand which can be found there every few miles. What if each of these towns had to support the roads of an area almost as large as Rhode Island, Connecticut, and Delaware? Roads would have to be cheap; dips would replace trestles and culverts; grades would not be uniform but would vary with the contour of the country; surfaces would be left in their natural conditions.

Railroads enter only the western part of Owyhee. Less than twenty-five miles of track, a branch line from Oregon on the Union Pacific to Homedale and Marsing, comprises the county railroad system. Highways must handle the people and the goods imported and exported.

Fortunately, the kinds of roads needed for the major part of the county are built without too much difficulty. In the more isolated sections they are little more than wide trails. A bulldozer scrapes them out; they follow the ups and downs of the terrain, meandering here and there to avoid rock and steep rises. If they become badly rutted and worn the road supervisor has his choice of two methods—he can repair the old one or he can knock out another one alongside. If they are easy to build, they are as easy to destroy, and a severe flash storm may rip out as much as a mile of grade. Such a storm may tie up traffic, but possibly the whole use of the road is by two or three ranchers who, accustomed to such troubles, keep stocked up with provisions and other necessities. Many a family knows that once the fall rains have softened even a short section of the road, they might as well block up the truck and let the air out of the tires for they are shut off for the winter. These roads run everywhere throughout the unfenced desert. One day we looked at some of them from a hill on the main north and south road.

We had not parked at a high spot where we could see miles of roads and trails below us in order to discuss Owyhee transportation methods. We had stopped because we wanted to eat lunch. But our hunger had not prevented us from taking the time to get to a good, sweeping view. All day we worked with miles of open country about, but we were not satisfied. We wanted additional distance; to look over the hill which stood to the south; to see the glistening white badlands that were once ancient lake-bed shores. The actual height of our noon sites mattered little; if the lunch spot was fifteen hundred feet high and the country around was a thousand feet, we were content to sit and inspect the panorama. If the spot was six thousand feet and other close peaks were sixty-five hundred, we lost the sense of domination and moved quickly from it. We could not follow such inclinations in choosing camps; they were picked for utility and not for scenic advantages, but we could always arrange our affairs so that we could take our rest in a spot we had chosen.

We left the car and found a convenient flat rock

where we could sit and spread our simple food. While we ate, we spent an hour or so of absolute relaxation. Nothing I have ever done has been so effective in bringing me to a sense of my own littleness. I realized the senselessness of worry and found it easier to adjust myself to things as I found them.

Our after-lunch conversation usually came out of some chance remark. On this occasion Wyomin' ate his last cookie and said, "I know now just how Moses must have felt when the Lord took him on top of Pisgah and showed him the Promised Land."

"It must have been more promising than this to excite Moses much," said Doc.

"I'm not speakin' of it as farmland. Haven't we promised ourselves for several years that we'd look it over, and isn't that just what we're doin' now? I've promised myself we'd see what was alongside every road in the county, and some places where there's never been a road."

"That's a mighty big order," said Doc. "You can see a dozen trails or roads from this hillside. Look how they spread out; long thin lines meander along every few miles."

"They might not all be roads. Some could be washes or dry crick beds. The long line that ends against the low cliff in the hills to the west is one; roads don't end in such places."

"As a rule they don't," said Doc. "But sometimes they do. That one you're looking at—I'll bet ten dollars it's a road and not a dry creek bed or wash."

"I believe you're right," said Wyomin'. "I wonder why it ends there. Let me take your field glasses." He looked the situation over carefully. "I see now. There's a black hole above it and some tailin's below.

It's a mine, but it's abandoned. The mine house has caved in and looks like a chicken that has been flattened by a truck wheel."

I checked with the glasses. "You're right," I said.

"Roads fool you once in a while," said Wyomin'. "But if you see a little cloud of dust movin' along at a fair speed you can be sure that it's a road."

"It might be sheep on the range," I said.

"Sheep make a much bigger mess and move slower," said Wyomin'. "A thrashin' machine makes a lot of dust but it stays put. You can tell the difference at any distance. Once you compare them they won't ever fool you. When I used to ride in Wyomin', I figured there were lots of ways of tellin' the difference at almost any distance. A trail or little-used road may be mighty faint so you lose it in rocky sections, but you pick it up again as soon as it runs into softer ground; and even if such stretches are badly broken up, you can see they follow a regular plan and are hooked up together."

"Sounds logical," I said. I looked at the outspread country. The only surfaced road, with the exception of the short traverse that Highway 95 makes through the extreme northern tip of the county, was the one that our station wagon stood on, the new highway south of the Snake running from Marsing to the Hammett bridge. The others which lined the almost eight thousand square miles of the sprawling county were little more than graveled trails. They led to isolated ranch houses and to sheltered valleys, to water holes and to higher pastures where some grass could be found later in the summer. I could see that the roads looked different in ways Wyomin' hadn't mentioned. The washes usually had patches of vegetation subsist-

ing on moisture brought by occasional showers. They
followed the bottoms rather than the hillsides as did
the roads. There was no pattern to the washes; only
gravity determined a course cut in the easily eroded
soil. The creek beds could be traced by the greenness of vegetation even in the dry season.

Irregularity and lack of design marked the network
so plainly laid out below us. The roads or trails started from the main road and left for destinations unknown. I spoke of them as mystery roads.

"They're all goin' someplace," Wyomin' said, "to a
mine, a ranch, a corral, a pass. They may be mysteries
to everybody but the man who uses them. They may
take just one rancher and his family twenty-five miles
or more to the main road. Maybe they connect up to
a mine prospect where some fellow has been spendin'
all his savin's every year to do assessment work. Some
of them go to a corral or a spring or a low divide.
This desert road system is a strange one. I know how
it is in Wyomin'. It's a good thing the weather doesn't
get too bad. They wouldn't have any roads at all if
it did."

"How did they establish all these roads?" I asked.
"What was the early history of transportation? How
is it handled now?"

"I suppose the Indians located the first rough trails
and they followed them to their hunting grounds or
on their trading expeditions," said Doc. "Probably
they followed them on the warpath and when they
went out horse stealing. They really weren't built,
only marked by use. Because they were the easiest
routes, the first trappers followed them, too. Then,
as the trappers sought new beaver country, they established trails of their own. One of the first real trails in

Owyhee County was made by the Oregon immigrants.
It followed the south bank of the Snake River for
a ways."

The heavy loads hauled by the immigrants left marks
which still remain in some places. Miners wandered
over the country and discovered precious metals in
quantity. Towns sprang up at the seat of the discoveries and roads were built in to haul the ore and
bring in the workers and supplies. The roads had
to stand terrific abuse. Freighters and stage lines made
demands which brought about some improvement, if
not in the repair of the roads, at least in better and
more careful selection of routes. Ranchers came into
the country to raise produce for the miners. They
needed access roads. And so every road and trail has
a history, although it may be only the history of a
small group, a family, or an individual.

"Not very peaceful times, those days," remarked
Wyomin', "what with the Indians raidin' wagon trains
and runnin' off all the horses, and stealin' the winter
production of beaver pelts, and burnin' and killin'.
They broke up the stage lines which first came to
the mines and they made a lot of trouble. Then came
an influx of desperadoes and killers so that a quiet,
home-lovin' man had a hard time tryin' to be happy.
Hardly an old trail in this county was without its
killin's and plunderin's. That was the time the mili-
tary men came in and built a few roads and forts in
the West."

Doc pointed to a spot where four or five lines
came to a common point and then split again into
two. "That kind of a junction of roads and trails,"
he said, "has got me into a lot of trouble. I despise
them."

"Why?" asked Wyomin'.

"These local people feel that these roads are here for their own use. They can't imagine any stranger wanting to use them. So they never bother to mark them. Suppose you are sixty miles from town and probably ten miles from the nearest ranch—what are you going to do when you reach one of these un-posted puzzles?"

"Follow the most traveled road?" I suggested.

"How do you know which is the most traveled? It may start out on a little shelf of rock and look as if it was never used. The least traveled road may start in soft dirt and look all cut up and worked to death. You can't judge by looks."

"Use your dome and check directions by the sun. If you want to go north take the road that goes north," said Wyomin'.

"Sometimes that system works and then again it doesn't. What are you going to do if you take the north road, like I once did in that kind of a fix, and follow it for five miles only to have it swing and go due east and enter a canyon?"

"That is a hard one," admitted Wyomin'. "What did you do?"

"It was so late by that time that I camped for the night. I got up early and climbed up on the canyon rim and figured where I was. I should have taken a trail which started southwest. It had to start that way to get across a broken-up wash. After I got across, the road changed direction entirely and from there on I had no trouble. No road signs, half a dozen choices, and sixty miles from town makes a bad combination.

"I've found the best way to do," said Doc, "if you

do happen to meet anybody, is to stop and talk. Ask them all sorts of things about the country. They like to gab with you and they don't mind if you ask a hundred questions. They'll tell you about junctions and what road to take and about the bad stretches, and looking out for the big double rock bump at the foot of the hill, and the bog at Whipple's line fence. If you get advance information, you can avoid a lot of mix-ups."

The sun was pouring down on the little knoll. The heat produced wavering effects, so the rock seemed to be moving. The air carried the dry smell peculiar to the desert. I placed my hand in my own shadow. It began to feel cool as it might feel when I removed something from the outdoor cooler at home. When I moved it into the sun again it was as if a hot draft had struck it.

The hot rays seemed to be bundled in shafts which moved in straight lines without any attempt to enter the shaded areas. Except for the dryness, the sensation was that of a hand dipped first into cold and then into hot water. The heat was dry so that our faces and hands were parched and rough.

"It's no wonder people get mixed up on these un-marked side roads," I said. "The haze seems to be like some solvent working on the distant parts so they just fade into some mysterious background."

The background may not be mysterious but it certainly is historical. Owyhee is an out-of-the-way county tucked away down in the southwest corner of the state; but ever since Lewis and Clark came over the Lolo Pass to the north, the county has been filled with affairs of national interest. The tremendous mine developments, the Indian troubles, the

Oregon Trail along the Snake—all are connected with
the history of these roads. One who could look back
might see ox teams moving slowly with their heavy
loads, or stage drivers whipping their horses to bring
their load in on time. That is the way I thought of it.

"Traveling cross county south of the Snake River
is certainly easier now since they have just completed
the new road between Indian Cove and Homedale,"
I said. "Nobody will be lost on it. Local people
will get much good out of it. But we'll have to be
careful it doesn't make us soft and unwilling to take
side roads."

"Well, I guess these roads are plenty good enough
to get us around to do our work," said Doc. "If we
run out of territory which can be traveled by autos,
maybe we can rent a pack string and saddle horses.
You could handle them all right, Wyomin'?"

"I can handle them all right and I can ride all
right," said Wyomin'. "I used to ride seven miles
each way when I went to school come snow or freezin'
weather. I rode bareback and brought in stock when
I was six. I spent lots of summers in the saddle from
the time I was twelve. I can ride any ordinary half-
broke range critter and I don't mind doin' it, but
I sure would hate to have to look after a string of
pack animals in a country where pasture and water
is as scarce as it is in some parts where we're goin'.
They'd be on the move all the time after we turned
'em out to forage. Horses in hobbles get so they can
cross country as well as a man who has been prac-
ticin' up for the picnic sack race.

"Think how it would slow us up," he continued.
"We can finish up now in some place late in the
afternoon and move to a location sixty miles away

and be ready for work the next day. Horses would have to lay their feet down for at least two and probably three days to do that."

"You're dead right, Wyomin'," said Doc. "The old ox teams were still worse. When the equipment all held together and the country was fairly level, they might make up to twenty miles in a long day, but when doubletrees and reaches and wheels cracked under the constant pounding, they were lucky to make five. That kind of program wouldn't leave much time for work. I think we better stick to the car and trailer."

"One thing that makes me sure we'll get almost anywhere with our outfit is its clearance," replied Wyomin'. "These rocks on the road have a mighty mean habit of reachin' up under modern cars and snatchin' out a few of their 'innards,' and, as Frenchy Burrand said when he broke his leg in a bear trap, 'That's inconvenient.' But the steel plate under the station wagon and the extra clearance of the outsize wheels will take us any place a jeep can go—and that's sayin' a lot. So I won't start sendin' for my saddle and gear for a while, even if the road below us is the only north and south road built to stand up under heavy traffic."

"It's a range country," said Doc. "There's irrigated land to the north and there's irrigated land to the south in Nevada. There are modern towns in both directions, and you can find all the conveniences that Western towns have. But between, in the desert and off the highway, there's land that might hold Bedouins with their goats, or camels from Arabia, or llamas from South America. It's big and lonely and inhospitable from a stranger's viewpoint. But I suppose that since the automobile, radio, and modern household conveniences are standard, the people who live in the district have no sense of being isolated or inconveniently located. News and entertainment reach their homes promptly. Certainly they have prospered financially and can afford to take on the advantages which are available. On the highway, three tough-looking, long-clawed badgers may stand and dispute the right of way with us as they did yesterday, but in the ranch houses the family could be listening to the symphony."

We piled our luncheon papers and leftovers in a niche between two rocks. They burned nicely so that the place was as clean as when we had come. We put the spoons, cups, and plates in a canvas bag we had brought.

"I still say there's a lot of road," said Wyomin', as he took a last glance. "Don't you think so, Doc?"

"Unquestionably, and it might be a serious thing to break down. You wouldn't be in much different shape than a man seventy-five years ago—except you wouldn't be so used to walking. You'd have to stick to the main trail; if you tried to find a ranch on a side road you might have to walk forty miles, and then not find it."

"Everybody and everything has troubles," said Wyomin'. "A cowpoke workin' for my dad once told me about those javelinas, or wild pigs, that grew in Arizona where he came from. He said they eat prickly pears as a main diet. When hunters kill and dress 'em, they find spines stickin' out of their stomachs. When I said it seemed like hard luck, he said it was, but it had one good point; if they wanted to scratch themselves, all they had to do was burp."

"Is that what you call a scientific observation?" asked Doc.

We got into the car before Wyomin' answered. "That, I'll let you, with your years of experience and superior trainin', judge for yourself."

CHAPTER VIII

Doings in the Dunes

Thirty per cent of the earth's land surface is estimated to be desert. Of this tremendous area less than 10 per cent is classed as sand desert; and of this 10 per cent a small part is dune country. And yet the man who has not been in contact with deserts generally thinks of them as a series of great sand waves which shift in violent storms, progressing slowly but inexorably, overwhelming camel trails, shrubs, trees, villages, and the oases to which the villagers look for sustenance. The theater has intensified this impression. The movies, even the documentaries, have done little to correct this opinion, which is perhaps natural, for the lights and shadows and the mysteries of the dunes attract more attention and provide much better photographic material than the flat, mosaic pavements which are almost as firmly fixed as the fields of more humid stretches. The dunes of the Saharas, of Death Valley, and of Iran—these are the kinds of pictures that the word desert brings up.

We had been some time in Owyhee County before we visited any dunes. But we had often passed a small but complete dune area which attracted our attention. It was easy to reach. Its long, heavy forms lay but a short distance from the Snake River, and there was only a brief succession of sand hummocks which necessitated leaving the car and taking to foot. Frequently we almost decided to stop, but we were busy examining the various parts of the county, collecting specimens and making notes on its ecology, which has to do with the relation of plants and animals to each other and to their environment—a process which required much time. Not until a young college student said that he could show us where he had twice found ice, nicely insulated from the heat of June by the surface sand, did we break our routine and pay the dunes a visit. He agreed to go with us.

After breakfasting and putting up a lunch, we picked up our guide and left town early one morning. Jackets felt quite comfortable although it would be exceedingly warm by ten. When the light appeared in the east, the moon was still shining. Blackbirds chattered as they made their morning flights. A few clouds hung close to the western horizon. A sparrow hawk occupied the top of a telegraph pole. The absence of dust, which would soon be stirred up by passing cars, made the air tangy and comfortable. Early morning has its compensations. A remark of Wyomin's echoed our sentiments.

"It would be great to get out so early, if you just didn't have to get up so early to do it."

We drove for an hour as the day awoke. When we parked our car a mile from the dunes, the sun had just appeared. Only the tops of the dunes were lighted;

the bases and flanks were dark and chocolate brown, and looked as heavy as solid rocks. They lay off the edge of the valley plateau, low enough so their tops almost reached the level of the plain near them. We loaded our notebooks into our packsacks with the lunches and camera and began our trip. Gordon, our college guide, led the way with a long-handled shovel on his shoulder.

Doc looked at the basin and the surrounding heights. He said, "It's easy to see why these dunes formed. The wind picks up the sand on the benches and hustles it along the upper slopes. When the sand reaches this hollow, the lighter keeps on traveling and the heavy particles drop and furnish the dune material."

The almost circular area was open to the river, and the dozen or more dunes were confined to a space of two or three square miles. They stood in a northeasterly direction, somewhat curved, bulky at the base and with tops ending in a thin edge which made a sharp outline against the sky. Among the dunes lay a few small, shallow ponds, from the edge of which a half-dozen jack rabbits bounded as we approached. They went lightly up the slopes in long leaps which appeared to stir up no sand. At the top of the ridges they stopped in the manner typical of their species and looked around unhurriedly before disappearing below the crests.

"This is a good hunting ground for coyotes," said Doc, "and a few of them are beginning to use it. People had nearly wiped the coyotes out in this section, but now they seem to be increasing."

"They poisoned and trapped 'em awful close," said Gordon. "They're so tough on sheep. But when you see how many rabbits there are and you figure how much they eat, you wonder if a few coyotes wouldn't be a good thing."

We walked in the hollow between the dunes, with their tops about three hundred feet above us. Little vegetation prospered, although some had managed to gain a foothold. Stiff, bleached remains of last year's growth still stood in some sections. When I bent a twig, there was a sharp snap as in breaking dry wood. A few low pink blossoms of the desert primrose appeared in sheltered situations. I did not realize the plants were connected until I came to a spot where a miniature blowout revealed a long root stock to which a dozen widely separated plants were attached.

Everywhere in the hollows where we walked the sand was covered with tracks. Big tracks, little tracks, small bulletlike holes, thin wavering lines, tiny imprints, closely grouped blocks of fours, and bird footprints which appeared with such closeness as to leave little space between them.

"This is a perfect recording place," said Doc. "Every animal has registered its presence and something of what it did. Look at the killdeer's tracks. I heard them near the pond as we approached. They probably came here to feed where the insects are thick. All of these tracks were made last night."

"Why do you say last night?" asked Gordon.

"Because in five or six hours we'll have a breeze to start these sand grains traveling again. They will wipe the surface clean; a late visitor won't see any signs of activity. This desert life isn't diurnal, you know, and if you sit here for hours in the bright sunlight you'll see almost nothing. What you might call night life is probably the most important of desert adaptations."

"Maybe we ought to see if we can find ice before the digging gets too hot," suggested Gordon. "If it's all right with you, I'll begin." He took his shovel about one third the way up the crestline of a dune. "Here's about where we found it before."

"You ought to find it again, then," said Doc. "What apparently happens is this: if you get a good snow followed by a cold wind which covers the snow with sand, then the following sands bury it deeper and in certain spots you have ice until, at least, the first warm weather."

Gordon began in a way which showed he was used to hard work. To dig a small exploratory hole was impossible, for the sand ran into it with the freedom of the contents of an hourglass. Before he had dug down two feet, the top of the hole was four feet square and a steady stream of sand poured from the margins.

I stood just below the sharp crest and gave the sharp summit a light touch. The sand ran down slowly with a grating sound and finally came to rest. Fanlike boundary marks on the surface indicated the amount of territory involved. I dislodged a larger amount with a kick of my foot. The resulting flow did not stop until it reached the bottom fifteen yards below, the sand at the top coming to rest while the readjustment at the bottom was still going on. It rippled and rolled, I thought, as snow does in an avalanche. The action of the sand was almost that of semifluidity; the slightest disturbance started an adjustment which ended only when it reached the angle of repose—which means the steepest angle at which it would remain at rest.

Every movement I made seemed to indicate that the angle of the dune was as steep as equilibrium would permit. I realized this more clearly when I took Gordon's place with the shovel. To get the hole any deeper seemed impossible; the removal of one scoop appeared to agitate the slope enough to bring down two scoops from above. To get deeper would require shoring. I plunged the shovel into the bottom of the hole and succeeded in getting it into the sand a foot or so down. There were no signs of dampness or of ice.

"We'll try it in another place," said Gordon. We moved higher up the ridge.

"You may not strike it at all," warned Doc. "There's no use in wearing yourself out. Maybe the snow went off this winter before a proper wind came along, or perhaps the snowfall was too light."

But Gordon persisted and between times I assisted. The results were as fruitless as before. We finally gave it up. The area was too large to test thoroughly. The snow must have drifted to produce the proper kind of a layer, and we had no method of determining where such a layer might be. Gordon agreed to try it again the following spring and advise us if he met with success.

We went back into the hollow. Two killdeers got up as we approached the shallow pond.

"These ponds are common in dune country," said Doc. "The rain percolates through the sands and, when it reaches rock or solid earth, it spreads out to form a little seep like this." He was examining the margins while he talked. A sudden movement with his hand in the water brought out a living object. "Here's a tadpole. It's a spadefoot toad, apparently, for it has no gills and has to come to the surface to breathe. They are specialists in this sort of habitat."

I watched it disappear in the aquatic growth as he threw it into the water. Somehow I could not reconcile the thought of frogs and deserts. A frog didn't seem to belong here at all. Even a pond among sand dunes conflicted with my ideas of a desert.

We walked directly across the smaller dunes, clambering with some difficulty up the steep sides. The increasing heat of the sun had made us remove our jackets and open our shirts. The still air began to take on that wavering indistinctness so typical of quiet and hot desert days. The freshness of the morning odors had been replaced by a heated oppressiveness which put a slight pressure on my throat. Walking, so far a pleasure, now became merely a part of the day's work.

Most of the life had, as Doc remarked, retired from the heat of the day. No more jack rabbits bounded up the dune sides, but a few grasshoppers buzzed loudly as they moved from place to place. By watching them I solved the mystery of the pea-size shell holes I had seen all over the smooth sand. A short-coupled grasshopper popped with force beside me. When it left, the pressure of its spring dug a neat little hole. I watched it several times; it completely demonstrated the origin of these pockmarks. As we searched further around the base of the few plants, we found holes in the sand partially concealed by vegetation. Doc said they had been made by kangaroo rats.

In the open spaces we saw a few huge black beetles almost two inches long and very much like the "stink" bugs which we occasionally get around our coast homes.

If we approached closely, they elevated their posteriors and we distinctly smelled their disagreeable discharge. I thought it no wonder that they appeared in the open so carelessly. Evidently, like their fragrant friends, the skunks, they felt secure against ordinary enemies.

We ate an early lunch. Gordon finished first and started prowling. Within five minutes he had located three horned toads, apparently smaller than those I had seen on the Arizona deserts. Whitish, unexcited, and passive, they submitted to examination without protest. When Gordon made a few shovel scoops around a bush, he was lucky (or skillful) enough to toss a kangaroo rat out with the sand through which it burst speedily and disappeared into another near-by burrow entrance.

The dunes appeared much different than in the morning; then, they had been cold and dark—huge masses only visible in outline; now, they were brown, full of warmth and sunshine. A burst of wind rustled the dry vegetation and made little hazelike sand fringes on the crests so that it looked as if they were smoking. In the hollow where we lunched we felt the sting of the sand particles on our faces. The furrows around us all seemed to move, each surface particle joining the others to make a brown syruplike effect. It was the morning eraser removing the record of the night before. The various tracks which had been so plain began to smooth out so that only unbroken ripples remained.

I had always heard that smaller desert animals could be more easily trapped if a furrow was made along the trap line. I mentioned it to Doc.

"Surely," he said, "and here's the reason." He pointed to the steps we had made just before lunch. "Look in them."

As I watched I saw the wind move small particles. Some of them danced lightly along and soon disappeared in the background. The heavier and slower moving ones did not clear the footprints but slumped in, and there they stayed. In this manner many small pieces of vegetation and heavier seeds found rest where they were no longer disturbed by the breeze.

"That's the answer, Frank. The depressions hold seeds and other edible stuff, and the small animals proceed to clean them out. I don't always find it so, but often small footprints prove that all of my tracks have been examined and their contents sampled."

I was beginning to feel as I thought a man was supposed to feel on the desert. The wind was now blowing briskly, but it brought no relief. The gusts reminded me of the time when, as a boy, I had spent many working days near the blast furnaces of a steel plant in the Middle West. My mouth was dry, my eyes ached, and my feet were a little swollen. "I don't think we are quite as well off as the animals that have slipped into their burrows," I remarked.

"You're probably right," Doc said. "Burrow life has advantages everywhere, but especially so in the dunes. When they go into their holes, they almost literally pull their holes in after them, for some of them have lined nests and many of them plug the holes to eliminate the indraft of the heat. And I have figures to show it works."

I had seen them. When the outdoor temperatures approached 125° Fahrenheit, thermometers placed in the burrows had registered figures of 60° Fahrenheit. The burrow then begins to warm up in the afternoon and early evening and, when the rat comes out in total darkness, the temperature is about the same (in the lower seventies) as the outside air. The surface of the soil cools rapidly during the nights and is coldest just before dawn when the rat retires to the burrow, which at that time is much warmer than the ground surface. The burrow then continues to cool off till the middle of the next afternoon.

The comfort of this air-cooled compartment probably explains why 95 per cent of Owyhee animals are burrowers. Among them are the ground squirrels, chipmunks, marmots, badgers, and mice such as the meadow, grasshopper, harvest, deer, and pocket mice. Also there are desert wood rats, two species of kangaroo rats, and the pygmy and cottontail rabbits.

Burrows had other advantages—for protection of the young, for housing during the dormant periods of estivation or hibernation, or both, and for storing food. Many animals temporarily use burrows for refuge or habitation. The large black beetle, so common in the Owyhee sand dunes, spends the hot part of the day in open-mouthed kangaroo-rat burrows. Lizards rush into them when frightened. Weasels and snakes enter them.

There is a wide variation in the dune burrows. Holes are of many sizes and lengths and are constructed in a wide variety of materials, from the soft sands to the hardest soils which can be dug. Many mammals appear to be particular about the soil they burrow in. The two kinds of kangaroo rats in Owyhee County are a sample. The Ord kangaroo rat prefers to burrow in soft, wind-blown sand and it is most numerous in the sandy dunes. On the other hand, the chisel-toothed kangaroo rat seeks harder soil with a dry, baked surface, or the puffy powder of the chalk hills, and will not be found in the sand. It builds mounds on the upper shore line of the bed of ancient Lake Idaho. In the sand the kangaroo rats will often have a part of their burrows rather close to the surface—apparently an escape method, for it enables them to burst through the thin layer when closely pressed. Roughly speaking, any soil which can be dug by a mammal will be used by burrowers.

Designs of the dune dwellers vary considerably, from the one-entrance hole and a single nesting apartment, to those with several entrances and escape exits, rooms for the young, for the storage of supplies, and even with drainage sumps. Some burrow entrances are finished by an effort to spread the excavated dirt, but in others the pile is left intact. We have seen no attempt in Owyhee at protection of the entrance such as is reported from southern deserts where the presence of cactus spines at the opening appears to indicate such design.

Every burrow which we pass in the dunes makes me think of the life beneath and of the activity of the area when the nocturnal appearance begins. The pace is fast. Predation is the rule rather than the exception. But life, food hunting, courtship, and other activities go successfully on.

CHAPTER IX

Desert Camping

The purpose of camping technique is the same whether a man is working or out for sport. Basically, the camper wants to keep himself comfortably fed and sheltered with the minimum amount of effort. The best campers discover or adopt special routines to accomplish these ends. The routines depend on the type of country and the conditions which have to be met. All localities have their problems, which may include winds, rains, extreme temperatures, or insects. But, like the wild animals living in a particular habitat, man must conform to the demands of that environment. Many phases of desert camping are easy; others are difficult; but at least desert camping is different from any other which we have done.

The camper who visits all of Owyhee County meets a variety of conditions. As Doc wrote Wyomin' when he asked him to join us: "Elevations in the county vary from 2,000 to 8,400 feet and that means a wide variety of conditions. Rainfall on the lower desert is less than ten inches; in the Silver City high elevations it is over twenty inches per annum, nearly two-thirds as much as the average in Seattle. Day temperatures range as high as 120°; but often 70° or 80° less at night."

I agreed with Doc as to the wide variety. I remembered the night when we had camped at about five thousand feet on Sawpit Creek in the Silver City district. A thunderstorm hit us after a preliminary display of lightning which seemed to originate directly above and struck all around us. Then came the wind tearing at our tent and snapping its sides with the report of a whiplash, letting go for a minute while the tent sagged before billowing it with a fresh gust of increasing intensity. Then the rain—roaring squalls of it striking the tightened canvas like drumstick beats —seeking passage but finding it only in the spots where tent props touched canvas. We were well guyed; nothing but a competently erected tent could have withstood the strain. We were well ditched, too, or the tent would have been full of water. We wondered, though we felt we had no real cause for worry, whether we were high enough on the creek slope so that no cloudburst, regardless of duration and quantity, could raise the creek to our level. It was a tough two hours, and when the storm left it was with the suddenness of its coming.

I also remember a storm on the lower plain. There the wind blew with equal intensity but brought sheets of sand whose movement was constant and so regularly replaced that there was, in effect, a three- or four-foot wall of sand visible. It was hot, sharp, and pervading. In an hour sand had entered every remote corner of our packsacks and our boxes, except

Doc's metal record cases. There was no peace under such conditions. Breathing was difficult; food was covered with fine sand. Dust clung to books which we opened or paper on which we tried to write. Both the Sawpit and this storm were in Owyhee County and typical of their location—but the contrast could not have been greater.

And how different from both these areas were those where we had spent so much time on Pilchuck in the Cascade Range in Washington. There, too much water is the problem. The firewood is always wet and hard to ignite and burn in camp. The bushes soak you as you brush against them. A dry camp is a rarity. The mountain thunderstorms come as in Owyhee, but they are not the principal source of rainfall. For days clouds hang close to, or even on, the mountain, and the steady drip sets the swollen streams to throwing spray high into the air. Clothes are damp and cold, bread will mould, and nothing but rubber keeps out the downpour. Hour by hour, without heat, or warmed only by the heat from the Coleman burner, we used to sit and work and wonder when the storm would break.

Water faces the Pilchuck camper continually. But it is good water—there are no sources of contamination. One can throw oneself at full length beside a stream with the certainty that the water is safe. In the desert, water is our greatest problem, because of its scarcity and because much of it is unfit for use. Even in desert mountains we found the water polluted by stock and we had to boil and filter it. Often we made dry camps with our only supply the water in our fifteen-gallon tank. Such a supply soon becomes warm and often acquires an unappetizing taste or odor.

The important needs on Pilchuck were waterproof
tents and flies and, for cooking, fuel other than firewood. We had to have a dry container for food and
we put everything that wasn't in cans in a place
where the bears could not get at it. One bear with
a keen appetite, and what bear hasn't one, can make
a shambles out of a summer grub supply and necessi-
tate another pack trip for replacements. Mould and
mildew, practically unknown on the desert, can be
extremely annoying on the west slope of the Cascades.

What are the special requirements in desert camping? How can a man camp so that he is fairly comfortable and keeps in good health, both of which
things are necessary if he is properly to pursue his
field investigations?

We don't go camping to eat. We try to spend as
little time as possible on food. We don't hunt for
a nice site along a shady stream and adopt as a program a little fishing, a fair amount of loafing around
camp, and a lot of energy spent on getting three whop-
ping big camp meals. We even neglect that most
romantic of all camping traditions—the campfire for
cooking. The pressure gas stove is better, saves much
time, cooks food evenly, and makes cooking easier.
We use a pressure gas lamp at night and consider it
an absolute necessity. It gives a fine light, burns little
fuel, and gives off enough heat in cold weather to
take the chill off in a tent.

Our purpose in camping, restated, is to make its
routine as small and unimportant a part of the day's
activity and time as is possible. How do we do it?

We know that the experienced and long-term camper carries a complete outfit, not as a dude, but because he has found that conveniences save him time

which is so badly needed for advancing his field work.

Here's a typical camp that we set up at Stoneman Meadows. There was no shade available, so we put the camp in the open with tarps for a porch. The tent, a nine-by-nine-foot miner's type (often called an umbrella), was placed in a grassy meadow at a spot about twenty feet from the creek and facing south or downstream. We used the door fly of the tent as a porch roof and we hung small flies on the side to provide shade. A small table and grub box were set up inside the tent, together with cots, air mattresses, and sleeping bags. The tent was tightly held by ropes attached to the umbrella ribs, a method of anchoring which takes it through every storm. Regardless of weather conditions we never fail to take this precaution, for a quick storm allows no time for preparation. We put a five-by-two-foot folding table in the porch and a couple of (would you believe it?) armrest camp chairs in the shade of the fly. We set the gas stove on the table while cooking.

Rarely did we sit on the ground and never did we spread our sleeping bags on it. Several times, when camping, we looked out in the morning to see a rattlesnake on the tent floor. In the juniper country of Owyhee, they like the comparative warmth of the tent interior in late summer. There are lots of crawling bugs, ticks, and other animals to consider. Mice may visit you if you are on a cot, but it can't be said to be a main thoroughfare for them.

Some people are depressed by the thought of the narrow menu which they think is an integral part of camping. In the old days, a grub list consisted of the prime staples—flour, baking powder, dried fruit, beans, bacon, and salt. Undeniably it was a monoto-

nous diet which was appetizing only when a considerable amount of time and skill was expended in its preparation. In addition, it was usually too heavy and lacking in necessary vitamins, although fresh air and sunshine probably neutralized the evil effects of such diets and kept the pioneers well.

The modern camper finds a vast array of canned goods, fruits, vegetables, meats, soups, and various desserts. They are equally convenient for use on the wet mountains of the Pacific slope and in the high dryness of Owyhee.

For breakfast we eat canned grapefruit, applesauce, or peaches, followed by coffee or tea, bread and oleomargarine, eggs or bacon. We vary the above with oatmeal, hot cakes or, rarely, trout, if we happen to be in high country.

Lunch is nearly always cold, with a choice of Spam, cheese, veal loaf, or sardines, together with crackers, potato chips, bread and oleo, chocolate bar, and oranges.

At night we may choose from the following: macaroni, canned stew, chicken and noodles, spaghetti and meat balls, baked beans, and wieners. Corn, tomatoes, peas, and succotash vary our vegetables. We usually drink tea and always serve bread and oleo. For dessert we carry canned fruit, canned pudding, and canned custards.

With the above menus as a sample, we have found no food problem. Its first cost is a trifle more than the old-style menu, but there is no spoilage and what is left from one trip can be saved for the next. New selections and ways of putting them up are always coming out, so we have a constantly widening choice. The weight of canned food makes it prohibitive where

back-packing must be done, or for other conditions
where weight must be considered. We pack our
canned goods in cartons and our loose material in
a tight wooden box.

Water is the great problem in the Owyhee country.
We had come from a wet mountain. Imagine, then,
the difficulty we found in adjusting ourselves to dry
camps, dependent on a small supply of water which
we first carried in a milk can until we found that
the abrasion of the tinned surface of the steel material
affected it so that it brought on diarrhea, a finding
that we did not confirm until we had unpleasant experiences. We discovered it only by omitting various
items from our food list but with lack of result, so
that we concluded that it must be the water in the
tank. A stainless-steel, reinforced tank removed the
difficulty from that source, although we had to watch
our water supply constantly. Standing water is usually
too muddy and alkaline to drink. The desert people
in Owyhee call drinkable water "sweet water," as
opposed to "poison water." All water is suspect and
should be handled accordingly. Running water may
be contaminated by stock. Water which is suspect
can be strained and boiled. Or one can use halazone
tablets and chlorinate it, producing a product so distasteful that many people prefer slightly alkaline
water to chlorinated water. The best source of water
is a spring, although not all are suitable because they
might be either alkaline ("poison") or hot. The rule
is to boil water unless it has a safe source. Of course,
the halazone and boiling have no effect on the mineral
content of the water.

The inconvenience of a short water supply can
be understood only by actual experience. We had

met it in some degree on the summit of Pilchuck late in the season, when the snowbanks had gone and water could be secured only by a long trip and sharp return climb from the lake which was the sole source of supply. However, we always knew that there was plenty of fine, sweet water if we wanted to go to the effort of bringing it up. But in a dry desert camp we economized in every possible manner. The car radiator had the first call, for our transportation was dependent on it being full. We had to go easy on washing, on brushing our teeth, and particularly in cleaning our dishes. Each of us had to present practically a clean plate to the dishwasher. Dishes were held down to a minimum—single spoons and sauce dishes serving a variety of purposes. Canned goods were heated in the original containers. Shaving water was limited to a single cup. Not a pleasant situation but a part of the adjustment which was necessary in such a habitat. No one grumbled. When civilization was again reached, our obvious appreciation of a plentiful supply showed how heavily the lack of water had been felt.

Insect pests have to be reckoned with. There are two shifts, but fortunately each shift has its own specialists and they never make a joint attack. As soon as the sun strikes the camp, the flies come out. These can be quite a nuisance, but repellents constantly become more efficient. At present, the repellent 6-12 acts very effectively against them. After they leave with the sun in the evening, the mosquito shift gets busy; 6-12 acts most efficiently in controlling them, also. No-see-ums have bothered us only at Jordan Creek in Jordan Valley. Repellents have done wonders for the camper and man who must work in all sorts of out-door situations. I can remember the early days when insects used to hang around us in a crowd and force us to choke and gag in smudge from a camp-fire in an effort to get rid of them, an effort which was only partly successful.

We occasionally picked up a tick or two but, by carefully looking for them once a day, we usually detected them before they burrowed in. Most of them are not spotted-fever ticks. In fact, spotted fever is uncommon in Owyhee County and few cases are reported. There is more danger from tick paralysis, which may result from the maceration of the head of the imbedded tick that has been broken off in the removal process. This can be rather severe. There is also a mild form of tick fever called "Colorado tick fever." The symptoms seem to consist of fever and chills for a couple of days, and a splitting headache that continues for as many more days. Doc had a case one summer. Certainly, to me, the tick is the most unpleasant of all outdoor pests—so unpleasant that my personal examinations have been sufficiently thorough to prevent their doing any more than wander over me; there is no way to prevent that. We have all taken tick shots, although few of the natives constantly exposed to them bother with going to a physician and having it done. The necessity appears no longer to be as imperative since some of the wonder drugs effect a complete cure of what was frequently, if not always, fatal in the past.

Other pests are not serious. Scorpions seldom bother, and their sting is not extremely annoying to the average person. Fleas for some reason seem to be rare, except on ground squirrels. Mice in camp are a nuisance, both because they get into all food not carefully protected and because they create a disturbance as they run around at night. Sleep in the wild is often interrupted by them. Several mice in a close space make an odor which Doc's keen nose always detects.

Porcupines in some places make trouble. For some reason they like to gnaw at the paint on the trailer, although they never touch the finish of the automobile. Often they make enough noise to wake us and make us get out of our sleeping bags. Sometimes it takes a gun to make an unusually bold one leave the premises. One we wounded after it had been driven away an annoying number of times chased Doc back into the tent after being shot and, as Doc had used his last shot, he had to stand on the bed and reload while the indignant animal wandered about the tent floor. That was not the usual type of behavior for a porkie, and we have never seen it repeated. Recently, rabid porcupines have been found, it has been reported—a serious matter.

In some camps, in middle or late summer, rattlesnakes can frequently be seen. We find them in the meadows where they are probably attracted by mice. Earlier in the season we find them on the slopes in the rocks, but as the heat increases they like the cooler grass. At Stoneman Creek one big fellow had coiled himself right between the tent and the trailer, which indicates that caution is always advisable, although none of us ever had what might be called a close escape from one. The fact that they do not always rattle when in deep grass makes them tricky. One should wear high boots in such situations. By leaving the trouser legs outside the boots, the snakes strike low and will snag their fangs in the cloth.

Small mammals may cause annoyance in some areas. The mantled ground squirrel is a minor pest that might be mentioned. It will often invade an unoccupied tent during the day. Trade rats, while common enough, have never troubled us, but we always take precautions against them by putting loose articles in tight containers.

We adjust our daily program to the country. Desert heat makes us set up a camp schedule quite different from that of the continuous day's work in cooler country. In the middle of the day we suspend work and sit in the shade where we read or write. After lunch we take a short siesta and we do not resume work until it cools off a little. Then we do field work in the late afternoon and after supper.

Desert camping, particularly specimen collecting and bookwork, is a job which many might find exceedingly unpleasant, but the pains we take to make ourselves as comfortable as possible relieve it of much of its hardship. And there are times when it is pleasant beyond compare.

I have spoken of not using the campfire for cooking purposes. But, whenever it is cool enough, we kindle a small one in the evening. The campfire at dusk is a pleasing, almost ritualistic affair. It's a holdover from the time when it played an important part in man's life—when it did his cooking, protected him from prowling animals, gave him light for evening duties, and provided him with warmth. Then, too, there was the feeling of safety and well-being that the fire provided—warmth for the mind as well as the body. Often, on light trips or emergency journeys, the campfire took the place of blankets and heavy clothing. The traveler would build a substantial fire, gather and stack a handy wood supply, and, lying close to the heat, occasionally would turn to expose a cold spot and relieve another which was too warm. I have talked to people even today who prefer to travel so light that they carry only food, a small blanket, an ax, and a gun. To them, a fire is the most necessary item.

To us, with our equipment and conveniences, the campfire has become limited to the nightly ceremony. But for us it does serve a most useful purpose. The campfire becomes a background of relaxation, a place for rest and consideration of the day's happenings, and a provider of opportunity to make future plans.

Some poet has called this the "witching hour." Whether the fire is one of pitchy alpine fir or the sweetly but acridly burning flame of juniper and sagebrush, the effect of the blaze is the same. If sage is available, we like to throw a few branches on the fire, just to get the wildness of its aroma. I have not seen the Basque shepherds use anything but sagebrush for their fires; it gives the camp a pleasant, rangy odor which seems to counteract the sheep and animal sweat.

This hour by the campfire is often the only opportunity we have for reflection. I once heard a famous philosopher say that lack of thinking is modern man's trouble—he is so busy he never takes time in his little life to give a thought as to why he is on earth. Albert Schweitzer has written that this will be known as a nonthinking generation.

My thoughts about the campfire have undergone a gradual change. When I first watched the sparks as they sought the blackness, I remembered the campers of past generations and I seemed to join the early settlers, the mountain men, the blue-coated Indian fighters, strongly scented with the sweat of horses and living on hardtack, bacon, and coffee. This may be why the latter-day cowboys stick to the range: they long to live as their grandfathers did, around the campfire in the open. It is this which holds the shy and taciturn modern young range riders with their soiled Levi's, blue denim riding jackets, well-creased, broad-brimmed hats, Spanish riding boots, and big silver belt buckles. They think it worth while to exchange the culture of the crowded city for the expansive horizons of the desert.

I have changed since those first campfires; now the evenings bring back thoughts of my past experiences, of hundreds of fires in different mountains and on the deserts. Many were pleasant, but even the unpleasant ones have mellowed with the passing of years.

One sees in the flames and glowing coals what he sees in his own mind. My most pleasant memories are those when, as a Boy Scout, we used to have a campfire every night. We always closed with the evening song which began, "Round our campfire's embers glowing bright," and we pledged to keep "Scouting memories true and dear."

There is still the promise of many more campfires to come, for the true camper never grows too old for camping. There is always one more camp to make.

CHAPTER X

Red Men and Mountain Men

The history of the whites in Idaho began one hundred and fifty-two years ago when Lewis and Clark, on their way to the Pacific coast in 1805, crossed the Rocky Mountains by way of Lolo Pass and entered the land of the Nez Perces. Though they were interlopers, the Indians did not give them a hostile reception. They welcomed them, a fact which they doubtless had occasion to regret many times later. The expedition remained just long enough to make canoes. It reached the Pacific coast in November. Lewis and Clark, on their return in May of the following year, held a great council of chiefs in the Kamiah Valley. This expedition, aided by the Indian woman Sacajawea, is known to almost every school child and has become an important part of the American tradition.

The crossing of the state was made in the northern third and a long way from the county of Owyhee, but it affected all hitherto unexplored country, especially that west of the Rocky Mountains. Lack of a suitable route had been a great barrier to the trappers who tirelessly covered the eastern slopes. The expedition discovered and mapped its course. It made reports of the country through which it passed. Travel over the Lolo Pass and subsequently discovered routes, and from the Pacific headquarters of the Hudson's Bay Company, received a great stimulus.

The present state of Idaho was included in what was then called the Snake Country, a rather loosely bounded area including most of Idaho, parts of southeastern Washington, small areas of Nevada, Wyoming, Utah, and eastern Oregon. But of this vast area this chapter is concerned particularly with the 7,648 square miles which comprise Owyhee, in the southwestern part of Idaho.

The great rush of immigrants to the Pacific Northwest occurred between 1842 and 1860, but there was little settlement and no agriculture in Idaho until mining began in the early 1860's. Before that time the only activity was the fur industry.

The Idaho fur industry was inaugurated when, in 1809, David Thompson came to Lake Pend Oreille and opened the trading post, called Kullyspell House, for the Northwest Company. In 1813 John Reid, of the Pacific Fur Company, built a cabin on Reid's River (now called the Boise River) but was murdered while trapping on its banks a few months later. The year 1823 saw the beginning of the Rocky Mountain Fur Company, with the famed trappers, Ashley and Henry, in charge. In 1834 the Hudson's Bay Company set up headquarters by building Fort Boise close to Owyhee County. Later, in 1838, the company bought Fort Hall from Nathaniel J. Wyeth, who had built the post four years before. It was located a few miles from the junction of the Portneuf and the Snake. Also in the year 1838, Francis Payette, of the Hudson's Bay Company, erected a second Fort Boise near the present city of Parma, Idaho. Though never a profitable enterprise, it was a well-known stopping place on the Oregon Trail. Both Fort Hall and Fort Boise were abandoned by the Hudson's Bay Company in 1855, nine years after the region had become a part of the United States. But in Idaho the first half of the nineteenth century was the period of trapping and famous trappers: Ogden, Sublette, McLoughlin, Ashley, Andrew Henry, Wyeth, Bridger, David Thompson, Donald McKenzie, Wilson Price Hunt, Francis Ermatinger, Bonneville, and Finan McDonald. These were some of the men who invaded the wilderness where beaver was king and who pursued their calling with courage and ability.

Trapping was the main activity of the whites in the Snake Country. Supplies came in and pelts went out by the cheapest and easiest method of transportation—by water, if possible; by pack horse, and later by wagons where water shipment was not practical.

The fur business, originally a matter of a man or two with a few traps and horses, expanded in size and complexity. In the large companies there was the main office in the East (or London), with district headquarters and various trading posts where pelts were purchased, supplies sold, and accounts kept. The actual handling of the fur collecting was done in several ways, among which were the following: by freemen who trapped on their own account and sold their furs to the company to which they were indebted for supplies or advances, by salaried trappers who worked for a certain wage, by Indians who

traded furs for supplies, and by private traders who bought and resold furs.

In extreme cases it was almost a feudal system, in which a whole group of trappers looked to the fur company for supplies and advances for which they were unable to pay if the catch was inadequate, or lost, or pilfered. In such cases the company was compelled to make further advances in the hope that a successful year would enable the trapper to clean up his debts.

It is not hard to visualize the type of man required to make a good trapper. Courage, strength, indifference to hardship, were prime requisites. A feeling for the wilderness, a faculty of orientation, and some degree of primitive mechanical skill were almost indispensable. Sobriety, steadiness, conservatism, prudence, and other conventional habits helped little in such a pursuit. Consequently the industry attracted many wastrels and adventurers whose recklessness would have been a great handicap in the settlements but which, in the wilderness, was rather an asset. These men worked like madmen during the season, never sparing themselves, and when they came out with their pack of furs they would often squander their receipts in a few days of wild orgy at the post or rendezvous.

The Snake Country occupied a peculiar position. The agreement which arose out of boundary quarrels permitted both the British and Americans to trade in this area. Their purposes differed greatly. The British were fur traders, not land colonizers; they wanted the country left open. They watched the beginnings of settlement by the Americans with distrust. They managed the fur industry conservatively, trying to perpetuate the fur production of each district by leaving breeding stock sufficient to replace the loss by trapping. But in the Snake Country they adopted a different plan. They wished to trap it out so completely that no Americans would be drawn to districts where they might settle down permanently. The men in charge of fur operations here were instructed to exhaust the fur supply in the area.

There were many competing traders and their operations greatly irritated a company accustomed to setting its own purchase and sale prices and to making its own decisions when grading the quality of furs. Rival companies endeavored to secure skins by making concessions. Such action could be controlled to a degree, but the worst of all trade inducements was the furnishing of liquor to the Indians, and in such a manner that the profits of a season were often exchanged by a befuddled native for a drinking debauch of a week or less. To the credit of the Hudson's Bay Company it must be said that they tried in every way to avoid such nefarious practices—but their competition showed no such restraint.

Such was the condition of the fur trade, the country's only activity, in the first half of the nineteenth century. On the one side was an industry principally out for profit and not always too fastidious about the methods used to obtain it. On the other was the native population which regarded the whites as interlopers and were now even actively hostile. The natives considered themselves a superior race; the whites, in turn, despised them and used their seasoned trading faculties to defraud them in many ways. Liquor was the key which would unlock the door to any native's furs, and the whites did not scruple to use it.

The natives of the Snake Country came from many nations. In general, in southern Idaho, there were the Bannocks, Lemhis, Sheepeaters, and Shoshoni who, in the southwestern part of the state, were called Snakes. The desert Indians of Owyhee were not of the highest type. They had been crowded into barren territory which made living difficult and forced a lower culture. Horses were hard to support and therefore not generally used. Grass dwellings, often without roofs, constituted their shelter. Large game animals were scarce, so they were forced to depend on jack rabbits and other small mammals. At times they subsisted largely on roots. Beaver were obtainable in quantity only along the Snake and the two other large streams—the Bruneau and the Owyhee— and their tributaries.

Such was the condition of Owyhee and its people. How did the Indians react to contact with the whites?

Space permitting, one could quote from a vast amount of source material. But lacking that space, it has been decided to confine the quotations to excerpts from the revealing journal of one of the most competent of Hudson's Bay Company men, Peter Skene Ogden, who should be known to all citizens of the United States because of his visit to the Indians who had perpetrated the Whitman Massacre and because of his success in having them turn over to him some forty American survivors. A large city in Utah bears his name. Trained in Indian dealing and knowing how to handle them, he did the impossible and possibly averted a war as well.

Peter Skene Ogden led expeditions into the Snake Country. On his visit of 1826 he crossed the north side of Owyhee County very early in the year and returned in summer through the south end. His observations reveal much of the country, its natives, and the progress of a fur expedition.

We quote only the pertinent paragraphs. Punctuation and spelling follow that of the journal, for which we are indebted to the Hudson's Bay Record Society for permission to quote.

Those who think of a trapping expedition in terms of three or four men with saddle and pack horses will be surprised at the size of the party which left Flathead Post for the Snake Country in the fall of 1824. Ogden's journal lists the names of 58 "freemen and servants." Their horses numbered 268; they carried 61 guns; and their traps numbered 352.

The expedition had been greatly hindered by cold weather. The horses were hungry and in miserable condition when they reached the confluence of the Owyhee and the Snake. The first quotation we make is from the journal describing their arrival at this point. The date was Saturday, February 18, 1826.

Severe cold it was late ere we started our horses many of them could scarsely stand this morning. Grass scarce in this quarter but wormwood [sagebrush] in abundance our Course South four miles when we reach sandwich Island River [Owyhee River] so called owing to two [or three] of them [Sandwich Islanders] having been murdered by the snake indians in 1819 this is from appearance a fine large River and from the upper parts not having been visited is worthy of examination—on the North side of the River [Snake River] nearly opposite to this Fork is Reid's River [Boise River] who was also with all his party to the number of eleven murdered by the Snakes and their establishment destroyed this party was in the employ of the Pacific Fur company subsequent to this Mr. D. Mc Kenzie made an establishment at the entrance of the River but from want of food and the   Natives hostily inclin'd it was abandoned and it was so far fortunate they did for two Canadians were killed only three days after, it is certainly gloomy to reflect the number of lives [which] have been lost in this quarter and without the death of one being reveng'd, not from the want of will but owing to circumstances which at the time prevented it and no opertunity [h]as since offered, but we must hope the Guilty must suffer both in body and mind. Hunt this day 2 Beaver altho 50 traps set. . . .

Sunday, 19th. At ten we started following the South Branch [Snake River] . . . . our route over a level country covered with wormwood and Sand and very few tracks of Deer two however were Killed one of the Companys horses remained in the rear with fatigue. . . . two Horses Killed this day in Camp for food.

Monday, 20th. . . . in this days journey no less than eleven Horses could not reach the encampment from fatigue. Late in the evening the four absent men that remained in River au Malheure [Malheur River] arrived with 25 Beaver but were obliged to leave four of their Horses. . . .

Tuesday 21st. . . . I this day came to the determination of sending back two parties with our weakest Horses to trap the Country we have traveled over. . . .

Wednesday 22nd. . . . It was late ere we started our Course east 12 miles and encamped on the Banks of the River. We had Rain last night and the weather mild compared to some time past but we have not had a calm day since we first came on this River [Snake River] 4 Beaver. . . .

Thursday 23rd We started at 10 A.M. our course on starting East 3 miles when we left the Banks of the River from the high rocks on both sides it was impossible for us to attempt passing we ascended some high Hills [Sinker Creek Buttes] our Course S. E. for four miles we then fell on a fine beaten Track in fact since we first reach'd this river there are no want of Indian Roads and from the number of old Huts no doubt in the Salmon season no scarcity of Indians but at present [there are] only a few starving wretches to be seen we followed the road seven miles and encamped on a small river [Castle Creek] destitute of Wood. . . . 1 Beaver from 20 Traps.

Friday 24th. We started early as there was no food for our horses in fact it is surprising to me they are not all dead constantly marching and for these last ten days living entirely on wormwood they are in consequence becoming very weak and cannot endure such treatment many days longer, we proceeded three miles when we again reached the main Stream [Snake River] and followed it in the hopes of finding Grass we continued on till night but in vain and encamped without wood [or] food for ourselves and no Grass. . . .

Saturday 25th. . . . we reached a large Fork called Bruneaus River a fine stream but bare of wood of any kind—finding two Huts of Indians we encamped. . . . so great was the scarcity of brush wood to kindle a fire that it was late in the evening ere we could collect a sufficiency. . . . 2 Beaver from our traps.

Sunday 26th. . . . it was near 12 oclock ere we started we on starting ascended the fork for one mile course E. S. E we then left and crossing over a point of Land again reached the Main Stream and followed it till late when we camped on a large Islande Isle de Cashe [Tyrrel's Island]. . . . on our travels this day we saw a Snake Indian and it so happened his hut being near the Road curiosity induced me to enter I had often heard these wretches subsisted on ants, Locusts and small fish in size not larger than minnies and I was determined to find out if it was not an exaggeration of late travelers, but to my surprise I found it was the case, for one of their Dishes not of a small size was filled with ants and on [my] enquiring in what manner [he said they] collected them in the morning early before the thaw commences the Locusts they collect in summer and store up for their winter, in eating they give the preference to the former being oily the latter not, on this food if such it may be called these poor wretches drag out an existence for nearly four months in the Year, they however so far as we can judge from appearances live contended and happy, and this is all they require. . . .

Monday 27th. . . . finding the river broad and wishing to cross to avoid rock and Stones we made the attempt and succeeded but the water breast high some of our property was wet but we were fortunate to Keep our powder Dry we again encamped on a large Island three miles in length and one in Breadth. . . . we took 10 Beavers and some wild fowl were killed and the freemen traded a broken leg Mare from the Indians which was also Killed so all together give a meal to the Camp and our poor Horses will also feed well tonight.*

On Wednesday, May 24, they reached the place where they had crossed on February 28 from the south bank of the Snake to the north bank and near the present town of Hammett. Wind and rain held them in camp on May 25 but they moved down the south bank on May 26, encamping for the night at "Isle a la Cashe." On May 27 they left the Snake and, led by an Indian whom they had secured as a guide, they started to ascend the Bruneau River. At this point we again begin to quote from the journal of Peter Skene Ogden.

Sunday [May] 28th. . . . this day we Started with the Sun and commenced ascending the Stream for 6 miles the River fine and well wooded when perpendicular Cut Rock [cliffs] prevented us from approaching it and we continued on until late in the afternoon when we reach'd a large Fork [East Fork of Bruneau River] but with cut rocks on both sides and it was with difficulty we found a place to descend and encamp [at Winter Camp] many of our horses greatly fatigued they had certainly a hilly road and Stoney—great discontent prevails in our Camp at my not following the South Branch [Snake River] and proceeding to Fort Nez Perces they [think we] will starve and we shall find no Beaver but our Guide says he will take us to a river of Beaver God grant it we certainly require it, it [beaver] certainly is becoming a scarce article in the Snake Country. . . . we certainly traveled over a barren Country today, not even a bird or the track of an animal to be seen. . . .

---

* On Tuesday, February 28, the party left the island and crossed to the north bank of the Snake into the county which is now Elmore. We will therefore leave them there and take up the story when, about ninety days later, they again entered Owyhee County.

Monday 29th We started early and continued following the bank of the River [Bruneau] without being able to descend from the cut rocks until the afternoon when we succeeded in descending and Fording it [at Clover Flat] and altho deep water all was safe across and we encamped our horses greatly fatigued and already many of them with swelld sides, but provisions are becoming scarce and we must continue on without delay in quest of Beaver if [we do] not horses will again be Kill'd I verily believe a more wretched country Christian—Indian or Brute ever travell'd over or probably ever will. . . . 1 Beaver. . . .

Tuesday 30th. Started early if we had cause to complain of bad roads yesterday we had still more this day one continued hill and gully covered with Stones and by the time we reach'd our encampment many [horses] were limping and others could scarcely crawl, we made several attempts to reach the River but could not succeed, and it becoming late we encamped on the hills, we are now fast approaching the Mountain [Jarbidge].

Wednesday 31st Started early and continued our progress. . . . Mr. Dears on a hunting trip this day saw two Snake Indians but on seeing him [they] soon secreted themselves, he made signs but all in vain, they are certainly wild as Deer. . . . 7 Beaver

June 1 Thursday. . . . I expected my guide intended crossing the Mountains here but it now appears he has no such intentions but is determined we shall travel over hills Gullies and Rocks for some days yet. . . . we were two hours in descending and ascending, we cross over the main branch of Bruneaus River [Jarbidge River] also two large Forks [East and West Forks of the Jarbidge] which discharge into it and at the later we are encamped again. . . .

Friday 2nd Started early & had not proceeded but a short distance when we met with a Snake, this Indian I saw last year on Bears River it was the rascal who headed the Party who murdered 9 Americans and pillaged them of all their property, and last fall again pillaged the Americans of all they had, it was rather surprising such a noted Character should not have attempted to conceal himself from us, [we] proceeded on with him as our Guide appeared to be at a loss but this exchange did not give us a better road. . . . we cross'd over three fine forks [heads of West Fork of Bruneau River] again this day with sufficient wood and water for Beaver but not a vestige [beaver] to be seen. . . .

Saturday 3. . . . Mr. Dears started this morning for an Indian tent with the hopes of trade but without success, in fact with the Snakes you must take them by surprise [and] take their property ere they have time to secure it [then] recompence them for it—by any other means you cannot obtain anything from them so averse are they to trade [anything] particularly Provisions—nor do I blame them as their resources are not great in such a wretched Country, nor would they remain in this quarter but [except for] the dread of loosing their Scalps should they remain in a Buffalo Country, they are certainly surrounded on all sides by enemies. . . .

Sunday 4th. . . . ground covered with Snow and still snowing and cold severe. . . . we again commenced our route by ascending a long hill [in White Rock Mountains] but not so steep as usual, very stoney, and in many places had the horses made a false Step they would have dashed to pieces. . . . all reach the Top in safty [safety] here we found a more level Country than usual. . . . Snowing and blowing untill the Evening, on our road we Stopp'd at an Indian Camp of Snakes and traded some roots from them and from their looks I presume they have nothing else to subsist on for more starving wretched looking beings I have never beheld in fact [they were] reduced to skin and Bones indeed for some time I was at a loss to discover if they were dead or alive nor would I believe it that human beings could be reduced so low without ceasing to exist Still they appeared happy and contented. . . .

Monday 5th. . . . no scarcity of Brooks and rivers [heads of Sheep Creek] and of the latter one of no inconsiderable size and depth and well wooded but as usual destitute of Beaver. . . . the guide gives us hopes of setting our Traps tomorrow we certainly require it our Stock of provisions are fast diminishing and one of the Freeman this day Killed a horse. . . .

Tuesday 6th. . . . we must hope Still to find Beaver and

reach our home at the appointed time in safty within the last 12 hours one foot of snow has fallen certainly most strange weather for the month of June, vegetation [is] at its full groth and today all covered with snow. . . .

Wednesday 7th. It snowed and rained all night. . . . still we Started. . . . when the rain and Snow encreasing, and at the same time finding myself seriously Ill I was glad to find so good an excuse for encamping. . . . In the afternoon we had a visit from 10 Snakes of the Plains the first we have seen this Year. . . . These fellows are far more shewy in their dress and appearance than the Snakes of this quarter. . . .

Thursday 8th. . . . at an early hour we started following the Fork untill its discharge into a fine large Stream [Owyhee River] when we encamped. . . . In the afternoon we had a visit from two Snakes. . . . I endeavour'd tho in vain to purchase a mule from them going so far as to offer 40 skins Indian Tariff in this lot was displayed all that could possibly tempt him, but I effected an exchange for a worthless mare without any expence, they have not the least Idea of trade and do not appear to lay sufficient value upon articles that would be of essential service to them, altho at the same time I am of opinion they have a good Stock on hand it cannot well be otherwise for within the last 10 months they have plundered no less [than] 180 traps from the Americans and Guns Knives and other Articles in proportion this with 13 men they have murdered since 1825 is sufficient to make [them] inderpendant of trade and this being secured without the loss of one of their Party—but the Americans are determined this season to make an example of them I do from my soul wish they may. . . .

Friday 9th At an early hours the Trappers started to visit their traps but met with no Success, ten men also started for the Indian Camp about 9 miles up for the purpose of recovering 2 mules belonging to an American [Canadian] Freeman. . . . untill an example and a severe one be made of them there will be no pease or rest. . . .

Saturday 10th. . . . we saw this day a family of Indians on the move they had no horses and were well loaded, Men, Women & Chilldren with roots [for food] they endeavour'd to escape from us but it was too late ere they discovered us they were allowed to pass without being molested this appears to be the season of roots in this quarter. . . . if providence had not given them roots to subsist on 6 months in the year they would soon perish for want. . . . 6 Beaver from 50 traps. . . .

Sunday 11th. . . . This morning our Guide intermated to us his intentions of leaving us [as he was] feeling anxious to return to his family at the same time informing us that the road was good free from stones and by following this stream [Owyhee River] it would conduct us to the South Branch [Snake]. . . . for the Past I rewarded him to the amount of eight Skins Indian Tariff with this present he was highly pleased and I am of the opinion had all Traders acted a little more generous towards the Indians they have been in the habit of employing the difficulty of obtaining them would not be so great as it is at present. . . . our Success this day amounts to 44 Beavers this enables all once more to feast . . . and gaiety and Cheerfulness reigns throughout the Camp. . . .

Monday 12th. . . . Trappers report who went in advance that the Beaver [trapping] is at a close and the River is closed in by high cut rocks simalar to those we saw on Riviere au Bruneau. . . . before many days the party will again be obliged to Kill horses for food. . . . This day we have finished [trapping] our second thousand [beavers] and if all our absent men are safe I trust they will add one thousand more. . . .

Tuesday 13. . . . I presume the Beaver are becoming scarce and if we are not more successfull we shall raise Camp although I am certainly at a loss what road to take, for the Horses that were on discovery [reconnoitering] yesterday from the effects of the Stones can Scarcely crawl this day. . . .

Wednesday 14th. . . . The Traps were collected. . . . we left the River. . . . I do not think we shall again see it, we trust entirely to Chance as we have no guide. . . . we saw a fine lake this day [Duck Lake] nine miles in length and two in Breadth. . . . the Camass root was to be seen in abundance. . . . Two Snake Indians well mounted came boldly to our surprise to the Camp. . . . they gave us some Idea of the road we should take also [informed us] that tomorrow we shall see a Fork of the River Owyhee on which there are some Beaver. . . .

Thursday 15th It froze a quarter of an inch in thickness. . . . when we reach'd the Camp of Indians we saw last night here some roots were traded and along our route this day the Plains were covered with women digging roots at least ten bushels were traded [by us]. . . .

Friday 16th. . . . we had no cause to be pleased with our road still less [did] our poor horses for it was one continued Stone from the time we started from our encampment and I am of opinion one day more of Stones will oblige us to leave or Kill many of our horses. . . .

Saturday 17th. . . . retracing back our steps 4 miles to an Indian Tent where I obtain'd a young man to guide us and then proceed on and I have no cause to regret it for [with his aid] we had a fine road compared to many days past. . . .

Sunday 18th. . . . we however succeeded in reaching the Mountain [height of land north of Wickahoney] crossed it and after descending it finding a small Stream [Jack's Creek] we encamped but not before we had a distant view of the South Branch [Snake]. . . .

Monday 19th We started early and at 2 P.M. reached our encampment of the 23 Febuary [mouth of Castle Creek]. . . . we are now again on our old track. . . . the Gentlemen of the Columbia in general as well as myself have now too often been led away by Indian reports of Countries being rich in Beaver which when they are examined generally prove to be false. . . . indeed an Indian can form no Idea of a Country abounding in Beaver a small stream with six Lodges appears to them inexaustable, and it is not with an intention of deceiving that they represent the Country rich, as it is to their interest to see us amongst them, but to be attributed to their Ignorance in not knowing better.

This ends the quotations from the journal. The expedition is about to leave the county. They had examined the country for its trapping possibilities and their conclusions are freely expressed in the record.

The trapping days in Owyhee are a thing of the past. Had the district been dependent on furs, there would have been little future for it. But, in the 1860's, a hitherto unsuspected asset was discovered in Owyhee and other parts of Idaho—mineral wealth of such magnitude that the future of the whole state was launched.

CHAPTER XI

Signs of the Times

We had intended to discuss certain phases in the history
of Owyhee County, but the actual talk came quite
without planning.

We were in a restaurant in the town of Nampa,
where we had come to provision, rest up, and enjoy
a little variety, part of which was to get a few meals
without having to prepare them. Not that we found
meal getting too irksome, but because not having to
cook them was a great change. I think we all realized that night why housekeepers get so much pleasure from an occasional dinner out. In addition, there
were no trap lines to tend, no notes to enter, no instruments to set, or readings to make. The restaurant
was only comfortably filled and there was no need
for us to vacate our table—so we could sit and dawdle
with our meal and hang over cups of coffee which
we sipped for an hour while we purposely considered
things not connected with our plans for the coming
days.

The conversation flitted here and there like a butterfly around milkweed plants. Wyomin's mention of the fact that we had seen three historical markers during the day turned the conversation to history.

"I suppose it's hard to know at the time just what steps are important in the history of a community, but it's easy to look back and sort them out, at least in a rough sort of way."

"Do you speak as a historian, Doc?"

"Not by a jugful. But the state is plastered with historical markers and other signs of the times. They are short but to the point. Each concentrates on a single event which is apparently isolated, but after you have read a number of them you begin to understand the design that caused others to do things that changed other things still more. I'm no historian, but it seems that there's a pretty good pattern of that kind in Idaho and Owyhee County."

"Exactly what do you mean by that, Doc?" asked Wyomin'.

"Here's an example. We see markers pointing out the old Oregon Trail, and then another marking the spot where Indians attacked a wagon train and massacred the immigrants. You realize how the first event caused the resentment that brought about the second. In another spot a sign points to an old stage route. You go back a little and find how the stage route was started to serve the first big mining discovery."

"That sounds logical," said Wyomin'. "The tables are almost all empty, so we don't have to vacate our seats. And the only movie in town is about a desert, and we've had enough of them for this week—so let's hear an amateur spout on early Idaho history. I'll pay for all the extra coffee it takes to keep you lubricated."

"I don't usually talk without reporters," laughed Doc. "But I can't conscientiously deprive you two of an opportunity to improve your minds, so here goes. Listen carefully."

"Take the state pattern first," he said. "You'll find markers on the route of the Pacific expedition of Lewis and Clark in 1805-6. They crossed the Rocky Mountains and were the first white men recorded in what is now Idaho. A monument refers to the coming of David Thompson, the first trapper, in 1809. The missionaries arrived in the early 1830's. A monument to the Reverend and Mrs. Henry H. Spalding was erected in Lapwai to the memory of these gallant and unselfish religious teachers who not only gave the Indians religious instructions but tried to teach them the rudiments of farming and the simple household arts such as sewing and knitting. The Oregon Trail is well marked both by monuments and memorials, and the trail itself was so deeply rutted and cut by the thousands of overloaded vehicles that the marks still remain after nearly a century of disuse. The discovery of mineral wealth gave the next impetus to a great development which is readily apparent all over the state."

"You must have been reading a lot," I said, after Doc made his brief summary.

"Only when I'm stimulated by road markers and signs and by the remains of early activities. They suggest interesting backgrounds, and I look them up. The advertising people would be pleased to know that people really do read road signs."

Doc said that the periods he had mentioned neither spaced out equally nor rated the same in importance. The trappers and fur companies followed right after

Lewis and Clark and, at the time, appeared mighty important to the West; and furs did make a big and profitable business. The Oregon Trail carried thousands and thousands of people through the state in its period of greatest activity, 1840 to 1860, but the passing immigrants did very little or almost nothing for the country. It was the discovery of mineral wealth in the 1860's that really started a boom. It attracted people from both the East and the Pacific Coast and produced millions in wealth. In addition, it stimulated farming and stock raising by providing a steady local market for the products.

Wyomin' hailed a passing waitress and pointed to Doc's empty cup. "You don't have to look in the pot, Doc, like you do in camp, to see if it will go around. So drink while you can. Next week you may be someplace where you will have to save the water that would make an extra cup and use it for a bath."

"The Owyhee history which particularly interests us follows the same general plan, but the emphasis is a lot different," said Doc. "The Lewis and Clark trail crossed in the northern part of the state and did not directly affect Owyhee. Because its streams are few and timber along them scarce, trapping was not good. There was nothing in the Snake Country to induce a passing immigrant to stop. The top item in the history of Owyhee is the discovery of gold on Jordan Creek in 1863 and the subsequent development of mining in the county. Booneville, Ruby City, Fairview, Silver City, and De Lamar sprang up. South Mountain became active. The mines produced millions. Horse-drawn freight and passenger lines hauled supplies from California, Oregon, and Washington."

"When we last saw Silver City, it didn't look as if it had ever been prosperous," said Wyomin'. "But it's like most mining towns. In Wyomin' I knew people who got dividends from mines just as regular as a rooster crowin' in spring. Then they'd get a notice that the mine had shut down permanently. It nearly wrecked some of them. That's the way the Owyhee mines ended up."

"It was good while it lasted," Doc said, "and if you go on the principle that it's better to have loved and lost than never to have loved at all, then it's all right. Certainly the people didn't have much idea that they would play out so soon. When you see little cars of ore coming out of a big mountain, you think it will last forever."

"The mines started agriculture," I said. "If you look at the files of the old *Owyhee Avalanche,* published in Silver City, you'll read about crickets bothering the crops and frost injuring the spring stuff. The mines must have been good customers.

"Michel Jordan, one of the discoverers of Silver City minerals, had a ranch. It might have been better if he had concentrated on the mine. The Indians tangled with him and he was killed. There was much trouble with Indians in that decade—and there was much lawlessness and robbery and murder on the mine routes."

"Well, the trail signs start you to investigating what happened," said Doc. "I remember seeing one at Walters' Ferry. As I recall it, the words said that it had been an important link in the Boise-San Francisco stage route. It told of an ambush and killing by Indians, and the death of the outlaw, 'Bigfoot,' a half-breed Indian who was lying in ambush with his band

and was ambushed himself while waiting. Then another time a stage driver, fatally shot, expired at the ferry."

"There's another at Murphy, the county seat of Owyhee," I said. "It tells of the fate of forty-four persons ambushed by Shoshoni Indians, a short distance to the east, and either killed or scattered. I've been at that place with Doc. It's a narrow, rocky spot on the Oregon Trail. The immigrants didn't have a chance."

"There's a marker at the site of the Ward massacre, also," said Doc. "Eighteen out of twenty people in a westbound outfit were killed. It's outside the county but only a few miles from where we are tonight. And there was the Van Orman affair on Succor Creek. Shoshonis ambushed the wagon train in 1860 and, when the battle was over, the wagons were burning, the stock and provisions taken, and nearly a dozen people were dead. And, of the survivors, about as many as were killed in the ambush afterward died."

I remembered a roadside monument we saw in the Bruneau Valley. We had gone by many times without stopping, but curiosity finally made us look it over. A small fence enclosed a plot in which the stone was placed. It bore this inscription:

> In memory of John and Emma Turner,
> the first settlers in Bruneau Valley,
> Sept. 18, 1869. Erected by their son
> and daughter, William Turner, Adelaide
> Turner Hawes, the first two white children
> born in Owyhee County.

We did not know about the Turners at that time. But before we were through we had found out about

them. They were good ranchers and equally good citizens. The daughter wrote a fine book called *The Valley of Tall Grass*. We all read it. I never pass the marker without thinking of people mentioned in the early days and of their life in that portion of Owyhee County.

People came in and out of the restaurant as we still talked. It was a place of courteous service. Nobody bustled about us with the idea of hinting that the table was rented for eating and not for a historical meeting. Coffee was freely offered until we refused any more. The crowd varied, townspeople in khakis and gaily decorated sport shirts, and ranchers in Levi's.

Wyomin' renewed the subject. "There's another roadside place that refers to the early days, though not in the happiest way," he said. "I'm referrin' to cemeteries. I pass them by in town, but in the country I sometimes stop at some little plot of ground on a sidehill fenced with fancy iron if the people can afford it, or sometimes with barbed wire. The grass is usually long and bowed over by the wind, and as brown as the dirt in the fields. Maybe there's just one stone; maybe there's two or three. They look neglected but they're not. The grass and the rusty fence and the hard ground are just as they are around their home places, and it could be that the relatives who are left don't want it any other way. They say, 'That's the way John had it when he was here; that's how he'd like it now he's gone.' "

"We've seen many of them together," said Doc, "but I didn't know you felt that way about them."

"That's the kind of a place where my granddad is buried," said Wyomin'. "That's the kind of a place he would have picked. No slick city cemeteries for

him. He was used to open country. He never wanted
to leave it. I always look at the stones and what's
carved on them. It's not a sad or gloomy reason. I
just wonder who the man was and how he got along
and what he thought of life—and what happened to
him. Only once have I got a direct answer. The stone
said: 'Died saving his brother.' "

"There's another way of getting close to the times,"
said Doc. "That's by reading the news items and
the ads in the early papers. If you look back at those
sections of the old weeklies, you can build up a picture
you can't get anywhere else. There are some files of
the *Owyhee Avalanche* at the State Museum in Boise.
What do you think of going over there tomorrow and
looking them over?"

Early the next morning Doc and I made the pleasant
drive over pavement to Boise, which during the 1860's
had been a mining camp and also the center of mining
outfitting in southwestern Idaho. We were courte-
ously received at the museum and the files placed at
our disposal. We found much to interest us.

Here is something about transportation in the early
1860's:

Messrs. Pierce and Francis, whose saddle train runs irregularly between this place and Susanville [California], connected there with their stage for Chico. They now carry the
U.S. mail through to Chico.

Travel cost:

The Chico and Idaho Stage and Saddle Co's train Chico
to Ruby City. Fare from Ruby City to Chico, Cal. $50.00.

There was a complete description of the route from

Chico to the Boise mining district and then the following advertisement:

A good ten mule team, two or more in company, can haul about eighty hundred of freight, with sixty hundred of feed, over this road from Chico to Idaho.

Fast freight schedules:

Schedule of Idaho Fast Freight Lines. Employs 21 teams, some of 6, some of 4, horses.
Umatilla to Boise City   6 days
Umatilla to Idaho City   7   ”
Six horse stage takes people from Boise City to Owyhee in one day [about 60 miles].

"This gives you a pretty good idea of transportation," said Doc. "Saddle-horse trains indicate tough going. Schedules confirm it, and ten horses and a small load shows the kind of roads freighters had to negotiate. Let's look at the ads; they will show the types of business represented at Silver City."

We found a wide assortment: an assayer, J. A. Chittenden; a restaurant run by "Wm. May and company with board $14.00 per week, single meals $1.10, invariably in advance"; the Silver City Meat Market; the Painter Company, printers; J. C. Holgate, General News Dealer. Much to our surprise we found the advertisement of a bookdealer, A. H. Webb, who advertised books at wholesale and retail. We wondered what kind of books, to whom he sold them, and how great was the demand?

Daniel McCleary operated the Miners Provision and Feed Co. We concluded that George F. Nourse, flour and commission merchant, must have done a considerable business in an area where flour was the basis of all food. DuRell and Moore handled general merchandise while Stevens and Summercamp sold wines, liquors, and cigars, and maintained a billiard table. Possibilities of litigation over mining claims may have attracted the eight or ten attorneys who at that time started practice in Silver City and Ruby City. These two communities were afterward consolidated under the name of the former.

In 1866 the professional cards seemed to indicate only the occasional visits of dentists, but Drs. T. D. Beckett and F. M. Denny, as resident physicians, protected the health of the citizens.

M. J. Abbott was available as a sign painter, and H. H. Tuttle followed what must have been the greatly needed trade of wagonmaker.

The first name of a government employee we found in the records was that of Sol Hasbrouck, who located in Ruby City as Deputy U.S. Internal Revenue Collector.

As might be expected, certain industries began early; in 1865, the beginning of the new sawmill of Bloom and Hard is mentioned. An August edition of the same year reports the stamp mills available for ore crushing. There were four operators, with twenty-seven stamps in use and a new ten-stamp mill in process of construction. A brewery was opened the following year.

"It's a fairly complete town," said Doc after we had looked over the list. "All the lines you would expect are represented. I wonder about the schools and churches." We searched for and found a few items.

School at Silver City closes because of resignation of teacher. School is badly needed.

R. M. Pease well known architect of New York and Owyhee
has been engaged to superintend the erection of the Union
Church and School building.

We could find only one mention of the number of
school children. It gave the population under twenty-
one years as 133.

Neither was church news too plentiful. We found
that church services were being held in J. C. Holgate's
building. A move to erect a building for religious
purposes was mentioned.

Other town activities proceeded at a greater tempo.
We found these samples:

Towards night a small portion of the community took it
into their heads to have a drunk and succeeded remarkably
well. Two fisticuffs at Silver City resulting in several black
eyes and the shooting of a dog in Ruby, were all the casualties
we have heard of.

French Philip leads his horse into a store. The merchant
swings a pick handle when Philip draws a pistol, and set
the rider and horse outside, Philip with a bloody head.

"That seemed to be one town where the customer
wasn't always right," commented Doc.

We read of the elegant supper given by D. H.
Jackson before leaving for the East; of the eighteen
guests at the course dinner which celebrated Captain
M. H. R. Slyke's thirtieth birthday; of the unusually
lively day for Silver City when boss packers, bull-
whackers, and others acted as if they hadn't had anything to drink for two months.

We pieced together a fair picture of amusements in
general.

December 2, 1865   Dancing party Wednesday night.
December 30, 1865   Snowshoe race challenge.

February 3, 1866   Meeting of Owyhee debating club. Sab-
                      bath school festival. Literary and musi-
                      cal entertainment.
July 7   "The July 4th ball was successful and
                      a fair proportion of ladies were pres-
                      ent."

January 19, 1867, an item states:

Amusements in Owyhee are principally confined to sleigh-
ing, sliding down hill on snow shoes and small sleds, playing, drinking, games, discussing matters of state and otherwise acting the stove sharp. Not even a hurdy graces the
scene and the field is clear. Such is life.

Crime reports in the 1860's, as now, occupied much
space. Two teamsters coming from Boise were stopped
on the road by two robbers not far from Olds Ferry
and robbed of $250 and a horse. Sluice robberies
were frequent between Ruby City and Booneville.
A poker game and fight caused the death of Tom
Wiltse. The store of Messers Moore and DuRell was
robbed. The Wells, Fargo & Company safe was robbed
of $5,800.

Much horse stealing took place. A dead Chinaman
was found. His people would not touch the body
or let it be brought into the house.

All such crime appeared to be regular and serious
but was overshadowed by the Indian menace. The
paper constantly carried news and comments about
the situation.

Trouble with Indians at the ferry crossing on the
Owyhee; Indians raid camp of William Stewart and
steal ten head of stock. They continue their thefts.

Battle with Indians on North Fork of Owyhee.

Indians make trouble on Reynolds Creek.

There were irate citizens in those days who, like Communists, thought that extermination was the proper method of discipline. The *Avalanche* printed the following: "The Chico Courant recommends the arming of a sufficient number of men to wipe out of existence the mischievous Indians inhabiting the eastern counties of the state, Nevada and Owyhee."

That a few farmers had moved in and started to raise produce for the mines is shown by some news items. Dow Vincent is mentioned as a vegetable man from Reynolds Creek, raising fine turnips and milk. Other ranchers were planting potatoes on Reynolds Creek. Melons were retailing for 12½ cents per pound. In 1866 it was mentioned that forty men had located ranches on White Horse Creek, thirty-five miles south of the Owyhee River.

Peter Skene Ogden's journal reports of the scarcity of game, years before, seemed much at variance with *Avalanche* news reports, which said that the mountains were full of game such as deer, mountain sheep, rabbits, grouse, and sage hens. Any miner who was a good shot could easily supply his camp with choice venison and wild mutton. One subscriber said that it only took an hour to capture a deer or sheep. Another remarked, "Coming over the mountains to the south of here, the other day, the party we were with scared up quite a few antelope, rabbits, sage hens, etc. Old hunters say that deer and other game is very plentiful this season."

We noted many random statements which we considered revealing. In the month of July and to August 22, 1865, Wells, Fargo had shipped dust, bullion, and ore to the extent of $27,744.21.

In less than eleven months an eight-stamp mill had turned out one million dollars in bullion.

Five stone cellars were in process of construction.

Laborers were in demand at $5.00 to $6.00 per day.

Master Masons meet at Tregaskis Hall.

Wood is worth $6.00 to $8.00 per cord.

County jail unfit and unsafe. Need for a new one.

Wanted—a bank in Owyhee.

Fires due to improper flues.

Shafts and prospect holes should never be left uncovered. (Had somebody fallen into one?)

Plenty of timber for mining in Owyhee. (Which would have been untrue had the mines held out.)

Hydrophobia among town dogs. (Was it brought in by dogs of white men and transmitted to coyotes and porcupines?)

A sixteen-ox team will haul between five and six thousand pounds from Susanville to Ruby City in thirty-odd days.

It was late, so we closed the file and left the museum.

"What do you think of Silver City now?" asked Doc.

"I feel as if I had visited it during the first boom," I answered. "After we assembled the pieces as if they were part of a jigsaw puzzle, there was the daily routine laid right out for us."

"That's just what I think," said Doc. "To me, all these scattered bits are just signs of the times. And because 95 per cent of Owyhee activity in those times was the mining centered in the Silver City district, the history of that area is practically the history of the county. I wonder if others who read the material think the same as we do?"

CHAPTER XII

Range Realism

The people who stopped their car in front of our camp asked for road directions but, as there was only one road, it was quite evident that they were merely curious about what we were doing. We were located on the high Owyhee Plateau at an elevation slightly over six thousand feet. To the southeast, the terrain climbed toward the Jarbidge Mountains. The grass was still green on these higher piedmont slopes, and across them could be seen the little dots which were cattle. To the north, the sun had dried the vegetation of the Diamond A desert. Our car stood alongside the road. On the sky line to the west, a pair of motionless horsemen, probably checking on cattle, scanned the area.

"Oh!" said the woman. "Look at those cowboys. Isn't that heavenly? I've never seen more interesting country. What a picture—cattlemen looking at their herds and their acres. Stock ranching; I don't know of a more ideal life. Where could you find easier work? It's independent, lots of room to move around in, and nothing to worry about. Who could ask for more? Wouldn't you like it, Bernie?"

Her husband seemed less enthusiastic, for he said nothing. She did not wait longer to rhapsodize over the desirability of the cattleman's existence. We had enjoyed the almost clear sky, spotted with a few cumulus piles over the highest mountains—just the kind of a sky that one always gets in the lush, Technicolor horse opera from Hollywood. But this scenery did not hold the travelers. They ignored it and were soon around a bend in the road. In town, they are probably still talking of the beauty of the scene and the life which they would like to lead if given the opportunity. To them it was a life which flowed easily, with plenty of leisure for sitting around, while the stock grew big and fat enough to be shipped to market.

Their departure made us comment. Wyomin' said, "It's funny what loony notions city folks can get."

"What's the matter now, Wyomin'?"

"That mushy woman. Talkin' about ranchin'. They think all a cattleman has to do is mount a nice animal and inspect stock. It's a new breed they're thinkin' of; it's never short of feed, puts on weight regular, and sells at a good price any time it's ready to turn off. They think stock owners haven't got any grief."

"Have they?" I asked, leading him on.

"Follow one of them around for a while and find out. You'll learn what it means to raise livin' things. It's a lot different from growin' grass or grain. Whether it's human or livestock, a baby makes work, and a lot of it, for the body who looks after it. When you have anywhere from a hundred to a thousand young ones, you never have any spare time."

"You think the matter's worth investigating?"

"I sure do. While Doc and I are runnin' trap lines, why don't you make arrangements with some of the ranchers and tag their heels for a while?"

The idea promised to be worth while. And so, in a few days, I found myself tagging after ranchers and learning about range stock. This particular property had been taken up by the Orland family decades ago. The original owners had kept it through good and bad times, until the four boys were able to run the place. The oldsters lived in town now, but the sons were active and they consulted their father whenever they saw him.

The boys had begun branding a couple of days before. I arrived at the corral just before noon and was invited to stay and eat. The wife of one of them had come over to prepare lunch. A place to eat had been fixed in some shade alongside the creek where there were three logs arranged in a U, about eight feet on a side. At the open end was a piece of sheet metal four feet each way, supported by large rocks and heated by a fire of dead aspen logs and branches. The food was cooked in large kettles and deep frying pans, all with lids and coated with carbon outside to a thickness which showed much service. This metal stove top was almost entirely covered. Except for bread and milk, the whole meal was a cooked one.

The boys and a Basque helper came in about one o'clock and really pitched in. They filled their plates at the stove and ate fast with little talking. Contrary to the impression given by range stories and shows, I have seen few talkative cowboys. As one old fellow said, "There isn't anything to say; one fellow can see what's going on just as well as another." They wasted no time. I was dallying over a piece of pie when they arrived, and they finished their whole meal just as I scraped up the crumbs on my plate.

There was certainly no lack of appetite. They ate hard-boiled eggs, pork and beans, and they did not refuse roast beef with boiled potatoes and brown gravy, with stewed tomatoes and corn as side dishes. They drank coffee and much fresh milk. I wondered about the milk. I had often heard of the stockman who had five hundred head of beef stock but got all his milk out of a can. Was it still the custom, or did modern stockmen keep milk cows? I intended to ask but overlooked it. Bread, butter, and jam, apparently, were as acceptable as if they were the sole items on the bill of fare. The only exception to a perfect cleanup was that none of them accepted both kinds of deepdish pie.

When I watched this astounding intake, I thought that the doctors who said that exercise had little effect on weight must be wrong. If not, why didn't these fellows have paunches like aldermen? Instead, they were of the typical bean-pole type of range riders. I figured they had to have that kind of build for they wore Levi's, the mark of their calling, and how could a fat rider get into modern built Levi's? They wore gray shirts and flat laloo hats and, when it was cool, blue denim riding jackets. Their complexions were dark and their faces long, with high cheekbones. There were four of them, Craig, Bob, John, and Slim, whose eight-year-old boy worked right along with them. Carl, the boy, must have been born with spurs on, for he was the miniature of his elders, wearing boots and Levi's and a hat like his dad's. He told me the saddle on his small bay horse was his and had been made for him. He did his work with all the serious efficiency of a trained hand. I thought I detected a certain pride because he felt he was doing a man's job. He appeared as fresh when I left as when I came.

After dinner they went back to a job which might have turned the stomach of the dainty lady who got so ecstatic about the life of the cattleman. I sat on the fence and looked at what would be plain bedlam to a newcomer. The dirt of the corral floor powdered to a fine dry dust when disturbed. It rose in little streamers every time a man walked across it, and when the frantic calves jumped and struggled I sometimes momentarily lost sight of the show. The dust got into my nose and lungs and choked and irritated me until I began to cough.

Then there were noises which were even more disturbing. When the calves and their mothers are separated, each sets up a bawling—the calf for the mother, the mother for the calf. This continued throughout the day until the various pairs were reunited. The bawling was loud, raucous, persistent on the part of the cows; higher pitched but equally loud and almost constant from the offspring. Both were equally unhappy, and neither hesitated to announce that fact. Would the clamor have disturbed somewhat the exponents of gentle, country living?

The boys appeared unconscious of the uproar. It was hard work, but they went at it, if not with pleasure, at least with unconcern. They confined their talk to the few words necessary to their job. They worked together well and with a precision which eliminated the need for the shouted and frequently profane directions which I heard at other brandings.

Nevertheless, they did not look quite as comfortable

as the two riders who had viewed the country when
the visitors had stopped. Would the strangers have
seen any glamor in this most important of all ranch
operations? I think probably not. Sweating, dusty
men with begrimed faces lose any natural attractiveness they might have when they are working with
frightened, bleeding, bawling, young, and uncompre-
hending animals who fight with all their strength and
are only subdued by the skillful force of their tor-
mentors. The fright of the other young animals must
have increased their own terror, and the efforts of
the cows to get back their young intensified the panic.

The day's routine was not a single operation but
a series of operations, where the animals were looked
over, given the necessary treatment, and a few pre-
ventive measures as well. Some of these methods were
used after a fashion years ago, but the application and
the effectiveness of the treatment have been measur-
ably improved. This was the routine as I watched it:

The cows with calves at their side (called wet stock)
had been picked up on the range and herded to the
branding corral. Here the cows were separated from
the calves and the two groups placed in separate pens,
which was all that was necessary in order to turn on
the day's clamor. The branding was done in an extension of the corral in which the calves were kept.
One fellow on a horse would ride up to a calf and
throw a lasso loop around its hind feet. The tightening of the loop and the movement of the horse
would pull the calf off its feet and drag it through
to the corral workers. When the calf was in the
proper spot, the men would jump on it and hold it
down for the various operations. The horse and rider
would keep a tension on the rope so that the hind

legs would be stretched out. Another fellow would put his knees on the sides of the calf and hold down the front legs. Usually the head would lie quietly on the ground with no need for control. A third fellow would hold the hindquarters down, and the fourth would do the cutting. If it had been done for pleasure or to torment an animal unnecessarily, it might have been called a brutal scene, but in reality it was a skillful and efficient operation done quickly and with a minimum of disturbance. But our tourist—would it have helped to confirm her opinion that the life of a cattleman was free and easy?

The many things to be done were taken care of in the following order: the cutting off of the tip of one ear; the slitting and notching of the dewlap under the neck; the removal of the horn buds and the application of a tar mixture to the wounds. A vaccination, performed with a pistol-shaped hypodermic needle, followed. Then came the castration of the male and the application of alcohol and more tar. Branding for identification and spraying against insect pests completed the program which, to me, appeared extensive enough to be called an animal clinic.

This seems like rough treatment for a calf that is still running with its mother, and for the moment it is. But they soon get over it, with infection almost unknown. There can be no denying that it is rather gory; from the time the ear tip is trimmed until the dipping is completed, blood flows freely. The slitting of the dewlap, locally called wattle, that pendulous fold of skin hanging from the neck of cattle, made the second source for a miniature blood rivulet. It is done by making a slit seven or eight inches long in the dewlap parallel to its margin and about an inch from the edge. This slit would be connected with the edge by a right-angle cut which would leave two loose flaps hanging. This alteration of the ear and the dewlap indicated at some distance that the animal had been branded and served as additional identification.

It seemed just about all three men could do to hold down the calf and take care of the operations. The blood streamed down the sides of the young Herefords and gave them a stricken appearance. But the first two incisions were as nothing compared to the dehorning. These were deep cuts, made down through the skin and bone, to remove the hornbuds, those small knobs which were the beginning horn cores. The operator made the cut with a tool that looked like two pipes partially opened and hinged at one end. By tightening the hinge and bringing the two ends together, the double tube which had been placed over the horn knob would close, cutting down and around the knob. Then the tar mixture was applied.

I sat on the dusty rails of the corral while the almost silent men co-operated as a unit in the performance of a hard, unpleasant task. They had started yesterday, and they would continue until all the calves were branded. The Orland boys were college men, graduates from the agricultural college of the state university. I wondered how many graduates in other fields would so philosophically accept what they would consider the most unpleasant aspects of their profession. I wondered how our acquaintance of the morning would like to cook lunch over an open fire, in dust to her ankles, and serve it under such conditions. Would she have modified her opinions of the advantages and blessing of the cattle-raising business?

The next step was the castration of the animal if
it were a male. A special cutting tool did the work,
the wound was daubed with alcohol, and tar was applied for protection. The animals had made relatively
little disturbance so far, but the branding which followed was objected to strongly. The operator in charge
of that work took the hot iron and placed it on the
flank with a sort of rolling motion, holding it until
the skin was well charred. A cloud of gray smoke
came from this application and mingled with the dust
of the corral. The odor rising from the combination
was a mixture of sweat, dung, sagebrush fire, and burnt
hide and hair which, to conform with the present
methods of the perfumers, might be designated as
Corral No. 5. Certainly, a stranger who had not been
squeamish up to this point would have found it advisable to get a whiff of air at a place slightly removed
from the scene of operations, but I sat it out. Pride
made me do it. I thought, if these fellows can practically inhale it all day, I should be able to withstand
an occasional whiff. So I sat tight and found that the
succeeding applications became less noticeable. Thus
do we become hardened to the disagreeable things
of life if constantly exposed to them. I think it would
have been asking far too much to expect a similar
reaction from the more delicately attuned perceptions
of the morning sentimentalist.

There were plenty of chances to have fingers and
arms cut and scratched. A couple of the men got
cuts and, evidently relying on the theory that what
was good for the goose was good for the gander, they
applied the animal disinfectant, sort of a milky solution
made of alcohol and some oil.

Man finds it difficult to compare his feelings with

those of animals, but more blood than hurt seemed to come out of the proceedings. Most of the bawling, or perhaps all, seemed due to separation and not to suffering, for the waiting calves made as much or more noise than those being worked on. The dehorning and castration were received without much evidence of hurt, and it was only the branding which upset them considerably. A stockman whom I once knew in Washington had this explanation to make: "I don't think branding really hurts them too much, but I believe the smell panics them just like a horse is panicked when you try to load it with a bear or a cougar."

Next came a short but extremely modern treatment against bovine disease—an injection by means of a pistol-shaped instrument. Compared to the rest, it was a momentary affair to which the harassed animals paid no attention.

Another useful operation was still to be performed. Warbles, fleas, lice, and other ectoparasites of cattle do much damage and cause the animals excessive annoyance. Spraying, while not permanent, is effective in reducing these pests. The cattle are run into a simple, tight-fenced lane just wide enough for a single animal. It leads to the spraying machine, a trailer-like structure with high walls large enough for a cow, and with doors at both ends. The cow enters the rig by a small ramp and then both doors are closed. A lever opens jets on the top and sides which thoroughly drench the cow. The animal usually struggles a lot and slips and stamps on the metal floor plates. The excess spray drains through the floor and is taken up for filtering and return to the reservoir. The frightened animals usually jump out of the open door rather than walk down the small ramp. They get another spraying later in the year.

That, briefly speaking, is what I found to be the usual branding procedure. Its complexity is obvious. Its difficulty and unpleasantness are equally so. The men told me they left the ranch at 4:00 A.M. and got to the corral at about 5:00 or 5:30. The riding horses then had to be wrangled before they would start out to bring in the little bunches of cattle, usually getting them to the corral about noon or an hour later. Branding would go on until late afternoon, and then the cattle would have to be driven out to the range. Usually the men started back to the ranch about 6:00 P.M. The work is exacting, tiring, and requires much skill and experience. It is a matter of pride with some of the ranchers to train their lads early so that, like this son of one of the Orlands, they can ride and rope before they begin school. I once heard a boy's skill around the ranch described by his father, who said, "He could hitch up a team when he was small enough to walk under their bellies."

The following excerpts from an article which appeared in the *Boise Statesman* will indicate the progress made by modern stockmen in the care of their animals:

A new chapter was written in Idaho aviation history yesterday when an urgent call from Tex Payne, a rancher at Fairylawn [Owyhee County], Idaho . . . sent Leo Snyder, Boise veterinary, winging by chartered plane to administer a blood transfusion to a prize bull.

Snyder, veterinary at the Blue Cross animal hospital of Boise, was contacted at the Western Idaho State Fair grounds and immediately enlisted the aid of Chet Moulton, Idaho department of aeronautics director.

Moulton said that to his knowledge the "mercy mission" to the small community . . . was the first of its kind in the state, although veterinaries fly to remote localities as a matter of course in their daily practice. . . .

If we left the impression that range life was all roundup and branding, our statements would be as misleading as the ideas of our morning tourists.

After the animals are branded and out on the range, the ranch work lets up and is confined to routine checking of the stock, moving them from one spot to another, and the many miscellaneous jobs which can always be found on a ranch. The Orlands handle their cattle on three ranges. During the winter they are taken down into the sheltered Bruneau Canyon. Apparently the climate is so different that grass, which comes up as a second crop after fall rains, remains green all winter and the cattle have plenty to eat, besides being shielded from the storms of the upper altitudes. In the spring they take them onto the spring range where the calves are born. At the end of June the calves are brought into the branding corral; then all are moved to summer pasture in a government national forest. The yearlings are gathered up the following year and trucked to the scales and sold.

Well, that's branding time without the silk shirts and sporty boots of the movies. That's what a man has to do who wants to make a living out of cattle. From our camp I can see the results of their day's work as a bunch of bloody and discouraged-looking calves go by. They have had a hard day, and, of course, they have not had the slightest idea of what it is all about, but Bob Orland says their hard times are over and, in a short while, they will be in good pasture and as well as ever.

CHAPTER XIII

Wyomin' on Overgrazin'

We pulled the car over to the side of the road so that Doc could take some notes. We found ourselves in the midst of vegetation of tans and browns which covered the sidehill until it reached a low crest almost a mile beyond. The cover was grass with long silky heads whose shiny richness moved in the light breeze so that the whole surface was one of glimmering smoothness resembling an Oriental rug. The occasional bursts of wind increased the movement and produced a continuous shifting of color pattern.

"It's a lovely sight," I said.

"It isn't bad to look at," admitted Wyomin', "but it's a sight that no stockman wants to see, although it's common enough. It's cheat grass and it's worth little for forage; just somethin' to fall back on in spring. Years ago you wouldn't find a spear of it in a lot of places where you see nothin' else now. You're lookin' at one of the bad things that's happenin' to the range."

"I suppose you agree with stockmen's reports that the range isn't doing so well?" asked Doc. "Many of the old-timers talk about how the sage has moved in and the grass has moved out. They claim lots of places have just about been ruined. Do you agree, and do you think it's due to overgrazing, as some say?" Doc got out of the rear of the car with his metal note case on his shoulder. He waited for Wyomin's answer.

"It's a matter of what you mean by overgrazin'. The range is meant to be used. No sane stockman keeps more animals than his range will carry in an average year. He'd be crazy to. If he did he would face buyin' feed, and that's dynamite. Some years, when conditions get extra bad, even the best ranchers have to work their range a little hard, but you don't catch them doin' it often. What's wrong about the range isn't that more stuff is bein' cropped off than grows; the trouble is that inferior and even harmful vegetation often replaces it."

"That sounds like a logical statement," said Doc. "Although most people say that the stockman has been too greedy and careless and his troubles are his own fault."

"I've been interested in range use since I was a kid," said Wyomin', "and I paid particular attention to it while I was in college. Of course, grazin' is responsible. All of the foreign weeds have come in since they started to graze domestic animals. The range isn't in the best of shape, but maybe any amount of grazin' would have hurt it. Maybe any grazin' at all is overgrazin'."

Doc put his equipment down and walked closer to Wyomin'. "I don't know exactly what you have in mind, but it sounds interesting. Just what are you driving at?"

"Doc, there's too much talk about overgrazin' by people that don't know anythin' about range conditions. What I meant was this: when likely and unlikely range plants nearly balance, almost any grazin' might be enough to turn the table in favor of the worthless ones."

"Just unravel that a little more, if you please," said Doc. He sat down on the car seat and prepared to take it easy.

"In the old days when the grazin' was light and there wasn't much close croppin', the good forage plants managed to hold their own. They weren't fed on to the weakenin' point. They could withstand the sage and other plant riffraff."

"What changed things?" asked Doc.

"Regular use of the range, but not necessarily overcroppin'. Worthless and hard-to-compete-with plants came in. Stock probably brought some—others were mixed with seeds. They began to crowd the forage plants that the local no-gooders were already about in balance with. Then the stock had to crop closer. That weakened the forage plants, but it was largely invasion and not overcroppin' that did it—at least that's the way I see it."

"It's an interesting theory," said Doc. "What do you think followed?"

"Maybe I can explain it in terms of lawn. It's not an exact parallel but it's close enough to show what I mean. Suppose that once in a while I let a couple of broncs nip around on the bluegrass around my ranch house. In good soil, the bluegrass could hold its own against the weeds for years."

"That's right," said Doc.

"Then suppose, Doc, I turned in two or three pet sheep. That would give the lawn a pretty good workin' over. Suppose they cropped too close so here and there a few almost-bare spots appeared. What do you guess would fill in those bare spots? If you think it would be bluegrass, you're wrong. No matter how rich the soil, the bluegrass would have little chance; a good stout dandelion or plantain would cover it in a jiffy. If you kept on, the grass would begin to disappear and the weeds would take over. Now, that wouldn't be overgrazin', really, but only in the sense that openin' up weak spots would let the weeds pre-empt the bare spots and cut down the grass."

"You think that's what goes on in range districts?" asked Doc.

"I think it's often pretty much like that. It isn't overgrazin' in the sense of puttin' too much stock in too small a space. It's due to hard facts. The stock feeds on good grasses and works it too hard; the animals dislike most weeds and keep away un-less good feed is scarce. That cuts down the strength of the always bothered forage plants and leaves the strong and vigorous weeds ready to occupy every new spot."

"That might be a reasonable conclusion," admitted Doc.

"It looks so to me, Doc. That's what happens in areas where every plant has to fight for existence. What we are doin' to stop it isn't quite enough. We concentrate on buildin' up forage plants so they can hold their own like they did a hundred years ago. We can't do it. Maybe the old boys who burned off

the range each year in certain sections showed more sense than we do."

"You don't think that burning was of benefit?" asked Doc.

"Of course not. It certainly did some harm, and maybe it did a little good. It probably harmed the grass less than the other plants, so it had a better chance to get along. It sure burned up all the shrubby stuff that has been hard to get rid of since it got so thick. It gave good and bad an equal chance each season, instead of forcin' forage to compete with untouched, long-established, vigorous weeds. In the long run, the cheat grass probably would have taken over. To blame range conditions entirely on overgrazin' looks wrong to me. It's only partly to blame. The system needs balancin'."

"Assuming what you say is true, what do you suggest as a remedy?"

"Get back to the lawn we talked of, Doc. How are you goin' to put it in good shape again? You can't wait until you have built up a good soil and re-seed so that the new growth will force out the weeds. That's theoretical and not practicable. There's one way to solve it. You have to cut down the worst of the competition. I think you have to use some kind of chemical controls. Try a couple of doses on the lawn and watch how quick the grass will respond, even if you let the ponies and sheep nibble on it."

"A lawn can't be compared to hundreds of thousands of range acres," observed Doc. He looked at his watch, but apparently only as a matter of curiosity for he made no attempt to move.

"I've admitted that twice," said Wyomin'. "But I do claim the same general principle applies to both.

You can't clear up either situation just by concentration on the care and quality of the good plants and failin' to do anything about the bad ones. It would be like tryin' to cure stomach ulcers without eliminatin' the conditions that cause them."

"It sounds worth trying until I think of the expense," said Doc. "Even at a few cents an acre, the hundreds of thousands of acres involved would add up to an enormous total."

"That's true, but don't forget it's a two-edged proposition, Doc. You have to remember that any increase in production on that same acreage would be a still greater total. You're dealin' in big figures. You have to think big and spend big. They headed off the Mediterranean fruit fly in Florida at an expense of over five million dollars. But they licked it in one big try. Think of how many millions they would have lost annually if they had let it become firmly established.

"It's just because millions of acres are involved and the expenses will be so high that we must do somethin'," he continued. "If we say the expense prevents us from tryin' new methods, we might as well quit the range altogether. It would be doomed. We are forcin' desirable plants to stand annual croppin' and displacement and, in addition, to compete with undesirable shrubs, annuals, and perennials. Each year the producin' capacity gets less and the problem grows. All sorts of undesirable plants come in."

He had heard of changes even among the new arrivals. Sometimes undesirable plants may be replaced by others which are even less desirable. Consider the latest plant arrival, medusa-head rye. It was first collected in Idaho near Payette in 1944. Now it is estimated that it has taken over nearly thirty thousand acres. The plant is said to have been found near Bruneau in Owyhee County in 1953. If it is a strong competitor, it may replace cheat grass in many places, which would be bad, for stock will eat cheat grass, while they do not like this rye.

"Every new circular or book on poisonous and useless vegetation lists a few newcomers," I said. "I suppose many of the poisonous plants have been introduced."

"But not all of them," said Doc. "There's records dating way back to 1825 when Peter Skene Ogden notes in his journal that the Snake Indians had lost four fine fat horses and his party one, due, it was supposed, to some poisonous weed."

"And I remember reading an item about poison trouble in 1863," I said. "In the Snake and Bruneau valleys the stockmen were forced to drive their cattle to the foothills to avoid a poisonous weed that grew in that section of the country. The item remarked that the appearance of the weed was almost a sure sign of spring."

"Did it give the name or description of the plant?" asked Wyomin'.

"No," I replied. "We can make only wild guesses as to its color, genus, and exact location. We don't know whether it grew on very dry or on damp ground. Its early appearance might indicate that it was poison camass. It might have been a local pest or it could have been distributed all over the Snake River plain. I checked other early material but could find no mention of it."

This discussion led to the general topic of stock poisoning by plants. We had learned that the stock in the area was subject to many hazards from plants poisonous in themselves and to those which were toxic because they absorbed harmful substances from the soil in which they grew.

There are many arguments as to the part which lack of suitable forage plays in the consumption of harmful plants. The stockmen tell us that some plants which are naturally unacceptable to stock are eaten only when desirable food is exhausted. Other harmful plants will be accepted if mixed with good fodder but will not be eaten if in solid stands. The sheep must be kept absolutely away from some plants. The sheepherder is usually close to his band and can avoid dangerous localities while the cattleman lets his stock run without supervision and has no such control.

Many are the ways in which animals may come to grief. Not infrequently, death comes from what can be called mechanical means. Sheep which have been on dry feed are turned into alfalfa pasture. If carefully watched, they come to no harm; but now and then the unaccustomed green food produces gas in such quantities that its pressure affects the heart. The process is so rapid that a large number can succumb before anybody knows what is happening. And there is another type of mechanical injury which occurs when stock takes on spiny food such as is found in some ferns and in cactus-like plants. A sufficient amount may cause punctures which are fatal.

Some soils contain injurious elements which are absorbed by plants. Selenium and barium are the minerals which cause the most damage, but fortunately barium is not at all common and, in Owyhee, selenium is confined to a very few small areas. The presence of selenium is usually indicated by the handsome plant, stanleya, whose large yellow flowers are visible at a distance. The greatest damage in these places is probably caused when the sheep eat species of the plant astragalus, which are commonly known as locoweeds because of the effects they produce. The animals become listless, stagger because of lack of muscular control, and die.

Many other plants may be said to be injurious in their own right. Approximately forty plants in Owyhee have proven poisonous or are suspects. They are not equally harmful, these enemies of stock. Horses, cattle, and sheep may be affected differently. Variations in season and the condition of the animal, in a measure, may influence results. Certainly, lack of good forage makes stock less selective and more likely to consume plants which may be harmful.

Plants operate quite differently in their attacks on stock. Some, like the larkspurs—considered the second most poisonous weed on the range in the United States—contain toxic alkaloids which cause constipation, prostration, bloating, and death. Wild onions do no damage physically, but they seriously affect the flavor of milk. Turkey mullein sometimes kills sheep because its foliage hairs form balls which obstruct the alimentary canal. Snakeroot causes trembles or "milk sickness" in cattle and dairy stock. The leaves of arrow grass and of mountain mahogany are thought to contain hydrocyanic acid, which causes poisoning. The juice of some of the spurges causes dermatitis, and when stock is feeding on hay which contains spurges it may have scours and die. One of the worst weeds kills sheep because the oxalic acid in its leaves combines with the calcium in their blood. This plant, halogeton, styled the "yellow killer," is

a native of Russia and is thought to have been introduced in imported grain, or by stock. E. W. Tisdale
and George Zappettini in Range Management, College of Forestry, University of Idaho, have written
a monograph entitled *Halogeton Studies on Idaho
Ranges.* We are indebted to them for much of our
information. The total area of infestation covers approximately 1,500,000 acres scattered over Nevada,
Utah, Idaho, California, Wyoming, Montana, and
Colorado. Of this acreage, about one sixth, or 250,000
acres, are in Idaho.

The first documented collection of this plant in the
United States was made in 1934 near Wells, Nevada.
In 1943 it was reported to be spreading in Nevada,
Utah, and Wyoming. The plant invaded the Raft
River country in Idaho about 1940 and spread rapidly.
It is a plant which appears early in spring, has an
extensive and moderately deep taproot, and vigorous stands produce eight hundred to three thousand
pounds of seed to the acre. Seed-trap tests showed
seed distribution at distances from 150 to 450 feet.
The occurrence of new patches at great distances is
thought to be due to the activities of man, and to
carriage by livestock. Halogeton appears to thrive on
the saline soils associated with salt sage and badly
depleted by overgrazing. Where the sagebrush is relatively intact, there is surprisingly little halogeton or
other annual vegetation. Prolonged overgrazing appears to have been the major factor responsible for
heavy infestations of halogeton on Idaho ranges. It
is sensitive to competition by vigorous stands of peren-
nial vegetation and is likely to constitute a problem
only where the native range has been depleted.

"The amount of loss from such a plant," said

Wyomin', "can be terrific. The direct loss is only one factor. Of greater importance is the annual loss which occurs because the land must be vacated. If the halogeton forces the abandonment of over a million acres, the land lies useless. Because it is useless, it becomes an added menace and a focus for the distribution of the poison-producin' plants. As these centers increase in number, the loss piles up. Sooner or later the pest will invade new areas and cause further abandonments, which at first sight might seem logical. If land produces toxic vegetation, just stay away from it."

"What is all this range deterioration leading to?" asked Doc.

"It's an immense problem," said Wyomin'. "There's a good many miles subject to plant invasion in Owyhee County alone. And there are many counties in Idaho and adjoinin' states."

"You put up a good speech," said Doc. "I didn't know you were such an orator."

"Anybody can talk on a subject he has a real feelin' about," said Wyomin'.

"Tell us what you think ought to be done," said Doc.

"I'm no range manager," replied Wyomin'. "Any conclusions I might draw would be as a sort of reporter talkin' of his own observations and what he learned from specialists. But I'd get together a tight organization composed of districts concerned with the checking and destruction of all harmful entries as its biggest job. The expense wouldn't be too great if it kept a constant check and acted promptly."

"You think that matters could have been expedited?" asked Doc.

"I'm sure of it. We hear of some weed that has just got a foothold in, say, Johnson County. It looks bad but nobody does anything about it. Then it jumps to Brown County: still no action. Smith County is next, and maybe it explodes and you hear of it in a whole state, or in two or three states. Early action when it first appeared would save millions for fightin' purposes. It would cost money, but this talk about expenses is like hearin' a timber owner complain he can't spend so much of his income to protect his holdin's against fire. Finally, he gets a blaze and not only his income but his principal vanishes. I'd make the organization big enough so that two or three states would be contributin'. Then somethin' could be done."

"Anything else?" asked Doc.

"You might have to use other methods and on a big scale, but that's what this country does best. It might include a scheme of doin' such things as fast railin' out and burnin' of worthless shrubs where there was a good possibility of re-seeding. Those shrubs have systems extensive enough to absorb most of the near-by moisture; I wonder if anybody ever tried to figure what per cent of desert moisture goes to useless plants.

"It would be worth knowing," said Doc.

"I'd set a scientific crew investigating the possibilities of really selective plant controls, and I'd give them money and force enough so they could do it justice. They might find some new deals which would stop the plants we don't need and leave the ones that we want. It would be a tough job, but the results would justify it. As I said about the lawn—you can't make a good one if you don't use some scheme to get rid of the unwelcome boarders. Wouldn't it be great to see a range where the bad stuff was movin' out and the good was comin' in, instead of the way it's goin' now?"

"Did you ever hear of a campaign like this being carried on successfully?" asked Doc.

"I never heard of any bein' waged on so wide a scale."

"You think it would be easy?"

"Did you ever try to clean the chickweed and crab grass and quack grass out of a kitchen garden and keep it that way?"

Doc said that he was one of the thousands who hadn't made a really successful attempt.

"Well," said Wyomin', "it can be done, but not many do it. This range problem seems like trying to keep a kitchen garden clean, except the ordinary garden is only part of an acre, while the undesirable plants have invaded many states. But a lot of kitchen gardens are as clean as a dining-room table. Professionals would be doin' the big job. It certainly wouldn't be easy, but I see no reason why a properly planned job couldn't do a lot to straighten up a condition that certainly could stand improvin'."

CHAPTER XIV

Foreign Deserts

In our search for material we did much reading about both foreign and American deserts. We wanted to widen our background so that we would have a better idea of the nature and use of deserts in other parts of the world. The differences we found in physical features were no greater than could be expected in regions having the common characteristics of deficient rainfall and mountainous barriers. Some are drier because they have a rainfall of less than half of the ten inches that Owyhee averages; some are much larger. But, in general, the comparisons are really ones of degree. To paraphrase the colored boy, "Foreign deserts are just like Owyhee, only more so."

But if we found the physical comparisons quite similar, the social aspects were absolutely foreign; everywhere we investigated we found tremendous differences. We learned that much of the desert country had harbored ancient civilizations. We read of chariots and war expeditions, of frankincense and myrrh, of caliphs and harems, of caravans and spices, of camel transport, of oases and roving flocks. We found some of the deserts still serving primitive people. In the Old World, desert life was of comparative complexity and carried what we considered, for such locations, a dense population.

In no place did we find this better illustrated than in an article entitled "Waters of Persia," written by P. H. T. Beckett and published in the September, 1951, issue of the *Geographical Magazine,* London. It covers only conditions in the Kerman Basin of Persia, but it is so well and feelingly written that we found it a moving recital of a hard-ridden population. We read it several times and with such approval that we wrote for permission to use parts for the purpose of comparison with conditions in Owyhee.

The Kerman Basin, elevation about six thousand feet, is situated in southeastern Persia, now called Iran. The author was the soil chemist of an Oxford University expedition which worked in the area. He begins with a description of a phase of the desert— a phase far removed from that of Owyhee:

Seated among a circle of friends in a garden by night, while the tea is passed in silver-mounted glasses and the talk moves easily, it is not difficult to feel with the mind of the poet:

Alas that Spring should vanish with the Rose!
That Youth's sweet-scented Manuscript should close!
The nightingale that in the branches sang,
From whence, and whither flown again, who knows? . . .

. . . About the lamp are the guests, their faces white in the light. Round where the light can hold back the darkness no further, are the moving shapes of the women, and the shining eyes of little staring children. From beyond is the sweet scent of the night flowers and the murmur of running water. Above the stars are bright and clear, "and that is why our village of Jupar is so high." The defence against the dark is so frail, and the comradeship is only for a night, so life itself becomes ephemeral.

Such is the picture of a Persian garden of the desert, seen through the eyes of a feeling observer. Then there is the desert itself.

Beyond the garden walls is endlessness, broken only by the camel-bells, as the camels . . . shuffle by and then disappear into silence. . . . And by day there is the bare desert, the *biyábán*—the waterless place where there is no rain from spring to autumn—with the loneliness of empty space, and the oppressions of an extreme climate and the tax-collector.

Then he writes of the background to be seen from the village:

. . . The mountains stand behind the desert, red between the blue sky and the buff earth. Here is the heaviest rain, and in winter the snow, and on the flatter slopes is the thickest vegetation. . . . Between the plants there is little soil and so the water from rain and melting snow runs off quickly, scoring gullies and waterfalls as it goes.

The above scene, except for the colors, is the desert as we know it. This is much like Owyhee. We could follow him down the slopes with a feeling of at-homeness. We know "the high basins and the valleys where the stony floor has gathered a little soil," but we recognize no social scenes such as this:

. . . little mountain villages, each with its well and stony fields. The stones laboriously gathered from the fields serve to hold back the terraces against the rains and floods of early spring. Above the villages on the tops are the sheep and goats, brought down to the fold at night and guarded by shepherds against panthers.

Owyhee has no crowding. The spaces are great, the residents few, and the villages are almost totally absent. We have scrambled down such places as those next described, but without finding anything similar to the lesser villages which Mr. Beckett pictures as typical of such surroundings in the Kerman Basin.

. . . They keep their herds among the hills, and in the valley bottoms grow corn and vegetables for their food, and opium for cash. In the houses the people with no land make carpets from the wool of the sheep, dyed with colours from mountain herbs. . . . Carpets, like opium, are good products for isolated villages such as these, since both of them have high value for small weight and so make adequate return to pay for their carriage to the market.

In Owyhee, livestock, wool, and hay constitute the bulk of the district's production and shipments. The residents, except for a few shopkeepers and mechanics, are ranchers.

Farther down the slopes is the best farmland:

. . . The foothills merge into the plain, and here at the fringe of the outwash from the mountains, just so far that only the finer materials carried by the spring flood have not been deposited higher, there is good deep soil free from stones, and with plenty of gently sloping land suitable for cultivation without steep terracing, but with slope enough for the irrigation water to flow the whole length.

Here Mr. Beckett describes another type of community not found in Owyhee:

... a fringe of larger villages, their surrounding lands nearly joining, and above the roofs of the houses the blue dome of a mosque or the bigger house of the landlord whose village it is. In the larger of them will be small bazaars, providing workshop and market for the tinsmith and blacksmith, carpenter and gardener.

Mr. Beckett does not mention the size of the holdings of these landlords, but since the tiny villages almost touch they must be very small. How different from the strip oases of Owyhee. Towns, usually consisting of a general store and post office and combined tavern and restaurant, are spaced miles apart. Here the few ranchers of the district pick up their mail and buy part of their supplies, the bulk of the purchases being reserved for weekly visits to the larger trading centers. The strips are not broken up as are the smaller parcels of the Persian village. In Owyhee they are occupied by stockmen for their home ranches where they raise alfalfa or grass for the winter supply of forage, and feed the stock in the shelter of the canyon. For these Idaho stockmen operate on a large scale which often includes the ownership of several thousand acres, the leasing of many more sections, and grazing privileges on high government lands where the summer grazing is good.

Greatly different, too, is the Persian method of bringing water to the fields. Mr. Beckett describes it in detail: the digging of the first *mother-well* where the gullies reach the plains; then, when water in abundance is reached, the construction of a long, horizontal tunnel called a *qanat* through which water is carried until it reaches the surface a considerable distance away.

Mr. Beckett notes:

. . . The digging is a skilled job, with its craft passed down from father to son; and often walking across the gravelly plain the traveller may see a group of men with their winch, at the head of one of the frequent ventilation-shafts, winding up sheep-skin bags filled by their comrades with silt from the floor of the tunnel. . . . Where the tunnel passes through soft sand the diggers set up an oven, and over a fire of desert scrub bake rings of fire clay to line the walls. . . . Across the waste are lines of shafts, showing that below there is a *qanat* bearing water from the desert to gardens perhaps twenty miles away. . . . And past the lines of shafts go the lorries bringing merchandise and passengers, and slow trains of camels from Meshed and the gulf.

We note that all the tunnel work is done without power hoists, mechanical conveyors, even wheelbarrows. The patient walk, the heavy load, and the steady effort requires weeks or months to do what one of our power excavators could do in days.

Regarding the method of disposal, Mr. Beckett writes:

At the point where the water flows from the tunnel into daylight is the focus of the village, the source of life, since from here comes all the village water. The landlord, who is the owner of the *qanat,* with responsibility to keep it in repair, will generally have some way of dividing the flow into several different channels. . . . Then each stream will flow from the garden to the next, under the wall of one and through the door of another, swarming off other streams as it goes.

With life, the water also brings death and disease, as it carries the offal and dirt from one housewife to the next, so the wise householder fills his tank of drinking water early in the morning while the water is still clear.

When the remaining water leaves the village it runs into the fields, where

. . . each patch is carefully leveled and surrounded by a mud embankment to hold in the irrigation water. Every patch is watered one day in twelve, as the ditches are opened and closed in turn. Near the village there is ample water, and the fields are tilled every year. But further down the flow will only reach the fields at the desert edge in a wet year; here the plots are fallow for five years out of six. At this distance from the house the melons and grain are very vulnerable to thieves, and parties of children with a few of the older girls build shelters of sticks and watch the crops as they chatter and play.

There is no such thievery in Owyhee, but there is much loss from other sources, especially that caused by jack rabbits which come in droves to the green fields, and by other animal pests such as chipmunks and ground squirrels.

Read Beckett's description of the areas about these small irrigated fields:

The bare desert surrounds the fields, cleaned of all its vegetation by the charcoal burners. It is not long since the green scrubby thorns grew to within sight of the roads, but now there is none and the sand dunes are blowing downwind onto the fields.

There are few places on the Owyhee desert entirely bare of vegetation, although the growth is not always of the most desirable type. The juniper, for example, has dotted thousands of acres in certain sections.

We come now to the days of ripening, which is in striking contrast to the methods in Owyhee:

At the time of the harvest for the different crops, between June and September, all the people seem to be out in the fields, cutting the ears with a sickle and piling them on a hard packed threshing floor, where two oxen will draw a wooden toboggan round and through the heap until all the grain is free from the ear. Then in the afternoon wind the grain and chaff together are tossed in the air, and all along the line of the fields are puffs of white as the men work away, until in one heap is the chaff and in the other is the grain, requiring only to be sieved.

Among the peasants are the beggars who come out from town at this season, bringing their empty bags, which they must fill if they are not to go hungry through the winter. They are all here: blind old women with neither husbands nor sons, leaning on their daughters' shoulders, "dervishes" chanting of Kerbela, and traveling musicians singing of Rustum and the wondrous heroes. By their heaps of grain the peasants stand strangely shy. Only on this day of the year have they such a store from which to give to these people even poorer than they, and there is reward in giving. But even thus the peasants will have so very little for the rest of the year that just a handful is a sacrifice as it is given.

Because there is comparatively so much in Owyhee, waste is little considered. The irrigating water runs long distances in open canals with no regard to loss by evaporation—a loss which modern studies have shown to be considerable. Only once have I ever seen grain separated from the chaff by tossing it in the air; that was in Mexico. There are no gleaners or beggars in Idaho to join the crowd at the harvest with the hope of receiving a few handfuls. Here the shattered grain is left in the field for the ring-necked pheasants and the small birds and mammals. If the vegetation is too short to be cut by machine, there is no hand reaping. Livestock is turned into the field to do the harvesting. I suspect that in those parts of Idaho where grain is raised, a strong wind shatters more grain in many a field than would be needed to supply a whole crew of beggars in Kerman Basin.

If the net results are satisfactory here, the matter of waste is overlooked.

No communal activity accompanies an Owyhee harvest. One notices the increased number of machines in the field. The power mowers cut the hay, the power rakes gather it up, and the power stackers put it into compact piles where it will remain until fed. Some of it is baled for convenience in handling and storage, but very little Owyhee hay is baled for shipment. So the harvest is just another period in a busy ranch routine. The population is adjusted to the procedure; no great influx of labor takes place, and there is no steady annual increase in the resident population. In fact the desert trend is toward a decrease rather than an increase because so many young people leave what they think is the monotony of the country and go into the cities.

Mr. Beckett writes of the division of the crop:

Once the grain is threshed the landlord or his overseer takes his share, in return for which he has provided seed, and water and the land, and from which he will pay the taxes. Round Kerman and in the South the landlord's share of all crops but opium is three-quarters, and four-fifths if he provides draught animals as well. . . .

After harvest,

. . . life returns to its level routine. The builder continues to make houses, the blacksmith returns to his forge to make files and spades out of broken lorry-chassis, and the weaver to his loom. In one village a kid was being fattened up for a feast at the end of September to celebrate the finding of the Ram in the Thicket; in another was a funeral as an old man was returned to the desert which had been pressing in on him and his for sixty years, and now could press but lightly.

And always morning and evening the muezzin calls from the tower of the mosque, and the name of God is passed from village to village around the plain.

In Kerman Basin, life goes on without change. But in Owyhee, the stockmen import blooded male stock to improve their breeds. They use all types of improved machinery to cut their labor costs, and their sons attend agricultural college to study underlying principles and new theories.

We were talking the matter over one night and Wyomin' said, "There's two ways of doin' the same thing. One has been goin' on since they started to irrigate by ladlin' water four or five thousand, or maybe more, years ago. The old way took care of big populations for a long time. The way it looks, it will keep on takin' care of them. What's your idea, Frank?"

"I can tell you what Mr. Beckett thinks," I said. "Here is what he writes":

But all is not well, and the peace of the gardens is threatened. Fields are being covered and villages deserted as the sand-dunes are blown from the desert. Some of the *qanats* are failing and landlords are not repairing others as they silt up or the roof falls. Some rich men dare not invest their money in new *qanats,* for fear of unrest, when the only good property is that which can be snatched up in flight.

So the water is failing and land is going out of cultivation: walking along the edge of the village lands furthest from the houses I found many acres that can have borne no crop for ten years at least, and now the only sign that they were ever cultivated are low ridges where before were banks to keep in the irrigation-water. Meanwhile the population increases, and the carpet industry which in better times would have provided work for the landless men is dying in the face of currency restrictions and import quotas.

So many men have neither regular work nor hope of finding it. The subsistence margin is so narrow, even when there is regular work, that for the jobless there is despair.

"According to that, the Kerman Basin has not fared so well at the hands of an earlier civilization," I remarked. "I wonder what kind of a lesson we ought to get from it? Is it in any way applicable to us?"

"It doesn't look that way at first," said Doc. "We have everything and they have nothing. But we must remember that the future of every one of our acres depends largely on the topsoil and the moisture supply. We continually get failures in both. We are invaded by weeds which poison our stock, by grasses much less nutritious than the kinds they displaced. Even today, in some places, we are fighting a losing battle. It may not improve. It may get worse in the future. It's up to all of us to see that the losses are stopped and gains made, for we must never forget—the land is everything."

CHAPTER XV

Bulls and Bull Sessions

Doc stopped the station wagon beside a large juniper tree growing in a pile of rocks near a bend in the road. Its branches overhung not only the rock pile but a considerable area beyond. Across the road, the ground sloped down into a gully which contained a small stream, one of the heads of Castle Creek. The air was full of the sharp, pungent odor which always marked the juniper forest. I remembered the Easterner in one of Zane Grey's novels who was given up for lost with tuberculosis and had recovered by going to the high country where he could smell the healing balm of the mountain forests.

Wyomin's quick eye caught the faint traces of tent-stake holes and drainage ditches as he put down the grub box on sand in which mica glittered. "I see that this is your old camp site," he said.

"That's right," answered Doc. "I've a lot of pleasant memories of this place."

As we unpacked our food our conversation was interrupted by a bawling sound, insistent and peevish, from around the bend of the road.

"Well," said Wyomin', "a complaint is bein' registered. We've discommoded some old range bull. I'll bet he was plannin' to occupy this shade, too."

The bawling became louder and closer. Suddenly the bull, an old and large Hereford, came in sight. Most of my experience with bulls had been with dairy animals which are often vicious and unpredictable. I asked Doc if this one had anything in mind.

"Huh," snorted Doc. "Sometimes I wonder if these whitefaces have a mind, they act so sluggish and dumb. If we just sit here and do nothing, that bull won't bother us."

The bawling continued as the bull looked at us with bleary eyes while it alternately approached and stopped. We sat perfectly still and pretended not to notice the animal. It kept on, passed the car, and paused for one final look just before it passed out of sight. Turning around, he gave a final indignant bawl and quickly disappeared.

"He just wanted to tell us that we hadn't spooked him," laughed Wyomin'.

"I think he's an old friend of mine," said Doc. "When I camped here earlier in the season, there were quite a few range cows and steers around. One morning when I was skinning mice, I heard a pebble turn and looked up to see that bull, or one just like him, standing about five feet away. Since the best policy seemed to be to do nothing, I just sat there motionless. After a couple of minutes, he turned and walked away. I noticed then that he had brought a cow up from the creek, spotted me, left her 'stashed' on the juniper slope, and had come to look me over.

After he discovered that I was neither cow nor bull, and wasn't interested in his girl friend, he went back and disappeared over the hill with his 'pickup.' "

Doc remarked that bulls were not always so easily disposed of. He recalled the time when he left the Riddle road northeast of Wickahoney and drove to a grass plateau. After some miles he came to a small bridge over Jack's Creek. He stopped the car at one end and collected a couple of ground squirrels. The disturbance attracted a bull which took its position at the opposite end of the bridge. For some reason the animal did not want to let Doc cross.

"What did you do?" asked Wyomin'.

"Probably just what you would have done. I didn't know what the bull had in mind. He might not attack; on the other hand he might have that stubbornness that goes with the expression 'bullheaded.' I couldn't afford to take a chance. The bridge looked sort of weak and incapable of holding a big load. What if he decided to charge the car and brought his ton weight across at full speed? I decided my business in that locality wasn't of much importance anyway, so I turned around. I've had such adventures since but never got into any real trouble."

"You've had a lot of fun with bulls," I said.

"That's right," said Doc. "But they're all in the day's work, along with a lot of other things. Every line has some troubles; I've always thought ours had a whole lot."

"We have, sometimes," said Wyomin'. "Why don't you tell us your opinion of the field naturalist's work and his problems?"

Doc fortified himself with a sandwich and leaned against a loose chunk of granite.

"Well, as you both know," he said, "this desert work is fine, but there certainly are some problems and disadvantages to it. Mind you, I'm not complaining. I just want to give you both sides of the story and I'll start with the disadvantages. From the collecting standpoint we have to fight heat, insect pests, and winds, along with a number of minor troubles. Heat bothers us most; it's the real problem of the mammal collector. It spoils the specimens quickly and thoroughly. Insects are the next biggest pest. Some of them, such as mosquitoes, bother the man; others, including ants and flies, injure the specimens. Then the wind may cause much trouble by covering the traps with sand. Flash floods have been known to wash out a whole string of traps."

"You make it sound hard," said Wyomin'. "What's the best way of meeting the problems?"

"You already know most of the answers. You have to adjust your work to a rhythm that meets conditions. Take heat, for example. We don't work what is considered a normal day. Because of the heat, I get up very early, run the trap lines, eat breakfast, spend the morning skinning and stuffing, eat lunch, clean up and shave, take a nap, then do 'office work' such as typing notes for the rest of the afternoon. Evening meal at five or a little after, rebait trap lines, take a walk, sit by a campfire for a while, read for a few minutes under the pressure lamp in the tent, and then to bed. It's a full day. Local conditions arrange it. I always thought the siesta habit was a lazy one until I visited southern Mexico and started work on the desert here. Now I agree with the adage that only mad dogs and Englishmen are out at midday."

We discussed the various problems separately. Doc

pointed out that the minor details must be adjusted as well as the major ones. There can be no delay in preparing specimens. They have to be skinned and stuffed rapidly, before they get soft. Also, because the delicate skins of small rodents dry out quickly, they must be moistened frequently with wet cotton, if there is a time-consuming rip or shot hole to repair.

Doc said that he had adopted a good system, which some California biologists had devised while working in Nevada, to keep specimens from spoiling. They cleaned out the viscera from the catch soon after they were taken from the traps. Then they wrapped the bodies in wax paper and enclosed the whole business in wet burlap. The evaporation from the burlap would keep the specimens cool and they could be held for some hours before preparation. He thought that if more hunters would clean out their birds, rabbits, and so on, just after they shot them, there would be far less spoiled game. He always drew chipmunks or ground squirrels immediately after taking them.

He paused to wave away a fly that had been attracted by food. "That's another pest which is an awful nuisance to people in our work. They blow the specimens in the trap line if you don't run the lines early in the morning. They bother chipmunks and ground squirrels so much that you have to visit the line often or the flies will ruin a specimen. Less flies are attracted if the skinning table is kept in the shade. It's hell to have to work in the sun. I remember once when an ornithologist and I skinned in a sunlit draw in the Sublett Mountains. We could hardly see the specimens for the flies that covered them. I learned a good trick to eliminate flies while skinning. The insects are attracted chiefly to the carcasses of animals already

skinned. As soon as I finish one, I toss the carcass
to one side and at some distance. Most of the flies
will be attracted to the carcasses, leaving the table
comparatively free. Then I bury the remains when
I clean up."

"Why don't you use DDT?" asked Wyomin'.

"Have you ever tried to fumigate the whole out-
of-doors?"

"Just inquirin'," said Wyomin'. "You haven't said
anything about ants."

"If you don't watch out, they'll run your trap line
for you. They seem to specialize on the eyelids and
lips of mouse specimens. Desert ants don't seem to
be particular as to species but, on Pilchuck, Frank
and I found that the ants would nibble on red-backed
voles until they were little more than a skeleton, while
the deer mice would be untouched. Another thing,
ants will go to work on a line baited with peanut
butter and, when you come back an hour later, there
will be just a little pile of brown powder on the
trap under the treadle."

"Any other insects bother traps?" I asked.

"Sure; there's a mean-looking devil which looks like
a big ant, has a color something like a bee, and a
head like a large grasshopper."

"You mean the Jerusalem cricket, don't you?" asked
Wyomin'.

"You're right," said Doc. "It seems largely nocturnal and has a taste for carrion. Often when I come
upon a mouse with a large part of it eaten away, I
have found a couple of these crickets under it. They
are ugly and vicious-looking insects. Sometimes they
will spring the trap and get caught.

"I think this ends the list of bad insect pests. Of

course, mosquitoes can make a man unhappy, but they don't spoil his specimens."

Doc said that windstorms in sandy country can put a layer of sand over a trap line and completely hide it from view. He had never lost a line, but it would be possible.

I remembered a time when Doc did lose an entire line, but under different circumstances. He was trapping in a dry wash and had put out traps that would cost about twenty-five dollars. A flash flood had occurred one afternoon and, when it was over, not one trap could be found. Another rare but annoying occurrence was the snapping of every trap by the big drops or the hail of a cloudburst, so that all there was to show for the baiting of eight hundred traps was a stiff back. Fortunately, most desert storms come along in the afternoon or early evening, so the line can be reset.

"A person who didn't know you would judge from your gripin' that you don't like deserts. You're not figurin' on walkin' out, are you?"

Doc laughed. "Oh no," he said. "In fact, I was just about to tell you all the reasons why I like it. Sometimes it's hard to take the extreme heat, which really bothers me, but the advantages will just about even off the disadvantages, and maybe leave a little to the good. The heat, for example, is more than offset by the cold and unpleasantness of the bad weather that visits the Cascades. I've worked in coastal ranges where my fingers would be so stiff they could hardly hold my skinning instruments, while water from a saturated canvas would drip down my back. This predictable Owyhee Desert weather is worth a whole lot."

"In what way?" asked Wyomin'.

"I can plan my work so much easier. If I want to trap an area for six consecutive nights, I can go ahead without having a stormy spell break up my trapping schedule. On Pilchuck, Frank and I would get the weather reports on my little portable radio so we could rush out our traps when clearing weather was announced. Bad days there were almost as common as good days in Owyhee.

"The mildew and mould of the Pacific coastal ranges is unknown here. You can imagine the difficulty of drying skins in the dripping tent I mentioned. I remember once when my ornithologist friend and I were collecting along the ocean at Westport, Washington. We were skinning and stuffing sea birds in cool and wet weather. We finally had to fire up the iron stove of our cottage so that we could dry out the prepared skins in the oven. Once we forgot about the 'baking' and had a couple of toasted skins.

"Plant collecting is much easier on the desert. Press the plants, change the blotters a few times, and the result is perfect. But imagine how difficult it is to press and dry a fleshy Pilchuck skunk cabbage. No problems like that here; I would say that it is the easiest place to press plants that I know of.

"Certainly Owyhee is a wonderful spot for our work, and in the deserts of Arizona and New Mexico there is even a greater variety than here. I would say that if numbers or density of population were the criterion of the habitat, deserts would rank in first place, as far as the small mammals are concerned. A walk around at night with a flashlight will give one an idea. These places are almost overrun with rodents."

"Any farmer could tell you that," said I.

"They don't deserve much sympathy. Killin' the

predators has been an important cause of the increase. We've hashed that out before," said Wyomin'.

"One of the most interesting sides of desert life is the comparative one. It's all very well to study a particular species, but I think it more fascinating and valuable to compare the habits, behavior, and so forth of a group of animals living together in the same habitat. Ecologists, you know, say that each habitat is comprised of a number of ecologic niches."

"For a bull session, this gets a bit technical," I said. "Suppose you go a little deeper."

"It isn't difficult. An ecological niche is merely a way of living. The meadow mouse fills the 'meadow mouse niche' just as the red squirrel has its own way of life which is different from that of the kangaroo rat. In other words, as a result of the process of evolution, for each niche there is a model of animal to fill it. Of course, evolution hasn't got around to filling all the niches yet.

"The animals and plants living together in a habitat comprise a group known as a biotic community. Right here, for example, the chipmunks occupy the juniper groves; the mantled ground squirrels are in those spalling rocks, like the pile across the road; pack rats stick to the rimrock at the head of the creek; deer mice are scattered pretty well, but close to the rocks; jumping mice and shrews occur along the creek; meadow mice like the wet spots where there is grass and herbs; sagebrush voles stick to the dry, grassy places; and deer and antelope feed on that higher ground to the south. By the way, aren't there four deer on the ridge now?"

"There were six; two just went over the hill," said Wyomin'. "While you were gassin', I was lookin'.

Somebody has to keep an eye out for Indians. What a mark we would have been for attack in the old days."

"You have both left out something about the advantages of the desert," I said. "To me as a nontechnical man, the esthetic side, the thing you haven't discussed, is the most interesting and pleasant of all. Where can you find such a panorama of life? You can stand on a hill and look at a vast animal population, from the low level to those almost at our own level. I can see burrow mounds of the chisel-toothed kangaroo rats, the sand piles of the ants' nests, lizards scooting through the rabbit brush, a hawk or vulture above. This is the living world, not the man-made cities.

"I like the pungent odor of rain in the sage, and the sweet scent of juniper that we have been enjoying this last hour. I like the vistas and the beautiful sunsets, and the dramatic approach of the great thunderstorms."

"You're right," said Doc. "All of these things may be trite examples, but they tell a lot about this world. I have read the books of the Alsatian philosopher Albert Schweitzer, in which he bases his philosophy on what he calls 'reverence for life.' Where can one learn such reverence but in a place like this? It may sound sentimental, but that is the way I really feel about the desert; and what is left in the world without emotion and feeling and reverence?"

Doc walked over to the station wagon and came back with a well-worn paper-bound pamphlet. He carefully turned its much-handled leaves. "This piece fits well with our discussion," he said. "It's from an account of the kangaroo mouse in the *Mammals and*

Life Zones of Oregon, by Vernon Bailey, the greatest of all field mammalogists:

It would be difficult to accord any commercial or economic value to these dainty little denizens of the desert nor can any serious sins of omission or commission be laid to them. Still they have a value sufficient to warrant many in making a long journey into the desert to gain a few specimens of a unique type and to learn a little of the causes that have guided its development along lines different from all other forms of life. As the writer looks back more than 45 years to the capture of the type of this genus and the first thrill of realizing its remarkable characters, so different from even its nearest relatives and opening up a whole new field of possibilities for the multiform kinds of desert life, it is no wonder that the hardships of bitter winter and scorching summer camps should have vanished before the fascination of this first-hand study of desert life. With all our intelligence and versatility of adaptation we are still far behind such animals in the perfection of physical mechanism for our needs, and we can surely learn humility if not wisdom from many of our inferior mammalian brothers.

CHAPTER XVI

Oasis

One thing which always puzzled our little group is why we never heard the word oasis used in connection with Owyhee or, in fact, with any other of our western deserts. It is used continually in describing foreign deserts, and there seems to be no reason for so localizing the term, for an oasis is simply a fertile or green spot in a waste or desert. There is much desert land in Owyhee; there are many green spots.

Regardless of the name given them, these green spots, or oases, make living possible and for this reason are of the greatest importance. The source of the waters which supply these areas varies. To be of value, there must be a supply of sweet water free of alkali.

One thing is certain; a dependable water supply is essential to any continued use of land. The eight- or nine-inch maximum rainfall received by most of Owyhee is not sufficient to support agriculture. Other sources must be depended upon. Where does the supply come from? is a question which is constantly heard.

It is a natural one. People think of deserts as dry and hot. A summer visit to Owyhee will certainly confirm this impression. But although the sources of water supply are scattered and limited, there are many of them in the county. We have driven for miles along the Snake River, the northern border of the county. We have seen the deep canyons of the Bruneau and the Owyhee. A small per cent of this water can be used to irrigate narrow strips of land, but the few streams of the county serve but a tiny part of the county's acreage. Elsewhere, other sources must be found. We have seen many of them.

We have seen shallow wells which are simply slight excavations dug to reach sources which seep close, but not quite, to the surface. Usually the supply is small. We have seen springs in various parts of the county. The head of Castle Creek, one of the larger creeks in the east central part of the county, is called Cherry Spring. The ranchers have fenced off the spring to prevent contamination. A water pipe leads into two large watering troughs. The overflow makes a small green patch which provides food for birds and certain small mammals. It supports a colony of meadow mice and pocket gophers. Deer and elk, as well as cattle, water there.

Many springs in the Owyhee Desert are hot springs. At the base of the Owyhee Plateau there are a number that come from water absorbed by the desert mountains and are liberated where the strata are exposed. In the Jarbidge area, the Murphy Hot Springs furnish a supply of hot water for a small swimming tank and a number of private baths.

Once we stopped at some beautiful springs at the head of Sawpit Creek, cold clear water pouring into little brooklets banked by luxuriant green moss and sedges. Almost every creek in the mountains heads at springs. In the heat of desert mountains, water from the snowbanks soaks into the soil very close to the bank and passes underground down the slope. Often a thin line of aspens marks the course. After a certain amount has collected under sufficient pressure to bring the water to the surface, it may appear in considerable volume.

The best artesian wells or springs of the county are at Bruneau. These provide water for excellent but limited hay farming. Some of the springs are warm and attract wintering deer. At Hot Creek, beyond Bruneau, a number of deer are to be found both in winter and summer, which is quite interesting as the surrounding area is so dry and barren. There are other springs of an artesian type at the escarpment, or sharp bluffs of the Owyhee Plateau along the Snake River bottom. Just below the falls on Hot Creek is a place called the Indian Bathtub because it was so used, and is sometimes still used today. A copious growth of poison oak surrounds it, as is the case in so many similar situations.

Temporary ponds occur during the rainy season where there are hollows and suitable ground conditions to prevent too rapid seepage. Some disappear very early; others last well into summer and, when they are dried, their location is revealed by the character of the vegetation which has been able to exist because of the moisture concentration.

Here is a typical water hole which we passed a short time ago on the road to Riddle. It covered

about two acres and was located in a rocky draw. It
had evidently been fed from the spring runoff of a
creek, but the bed of that stream was now completely
dry. The area was a natural reservoir with no outlet.
A sparse growth of shrubbery encircled it, growing
thicker closer to the hole. Willows and a thrifty
band of grass about twenty-five feet wide made up
the growth. About a dozen cattle, attracted by the
water and grass, grazed in the vicinity of the hole.
Several pairs of Brewer's blackbirds nested close and
a pair of killdeer constantly called while we were
there. Around was bare, dusty desert. The water was
muddy, gray-colored, and opaque, but it was water.

Higher in the mountains where the rain is heavier,
small ponds sometimes linger in suitable hollows and,
if the weather is favorable, may last through the season. They, too, are indicated by green margins of
vegetation.

The higher levels of the more favorably situated
mountains in the county may be called vertical oases
in the broadest sense of the term, for they are areas
which receive sufficient moisture to keep them green
much of the summer season, and they are surrounded
by desert which extends far up on the mountains
themselves.

By far the most important Owyhee oases are those
which, for lack of a better name, may be called "strip
oases." They are located in the canyons dug by the
action of streams. The stream lies on the bottom,
slowly moving back and forth in its braided bed (if
the floor is wide). When it cuts into a bank, the
material caves in and topples into the water. Basalt
shatters quickly on exposure to air and, in this area,
erosion is more a process of undermining and collapse

than of out-and-out carving. The action of the stream during the year is the slow grinding of the rocks in its bed and the downstream transport of the fine material.

The walls of the canyons are usually not solid rock, vertical from top to bottom, but consist of a series of terraces with each higher one set back from the one below it, thus making a series of steps which are continually modified as rocks of the wall of each step gradually split loose and topple. The shattered rock falls; if the slope is steep and active, a rock slide builds up; but, if there is little dropping, the slope becomes soil-covered.

For an example of such a canyon, we will use one in which we are now working, the canyon of the East Fork of the Jarbidge River at Murphy Hot Springs.

We reached it by driving several hours south over the Bruneau Desert, the driest and hottest part of the Owyhee Desert. The road curves little, pushing on for mile after mile across the gently rising plateau which stretches toward the Jarbidge Mountains, shimmering in the heat waves far to the south. Almost imperceptibly, they gradually come closer. Dust often covers the road to a depth of more than a foot, so that a great cloud of fine powder pursues the car and gathers and cascades off the rear window. Enough of it gets inside the car to clog our throats and noses.

It's a task, this kind of driving, and when the dust drops on skin wet with perspiration the result is most irritating. But nobody complains or even remarks about it; we know that it won't last forever and that it is part of the job. We are going fast enough to escape the worst of the cloud.

Wyomin' makes a cheerful remark. "This kind of

travel might be bad if a man was in a covered wagon and takin' the dust kicked up by the horses ahead. I don't know how he could manage to keep to the trail unless he sent a man to walk ahead of the team."

We agree philosophically if not cheerfully that we are not so bad off after all, but our conversation languishes and we settle down to wait out the discomfort. Lunch time passes, but we do not care to stop and eat. We do not have to wait too long.

Suddenly we reach harder road and a canyon opens up in front of the car; the road turns abruptly to the right and begins a long drop to the bottom. The walls are the typical basalt type with steps of steepness, and with sagebrush growing on the talus slopes below. We glimpse the river as it passes between willow-lined banks, with tall cottonwoods on the higher ground. The floor widens a bit here and there but, for the most part, it is a narrow strip with room for little more than the road and a narrow grazing space.

For the first time we begin to wipe the dust from our faces. We shake our handkerchiefs outside the open window—dust flies as when an emptied flour sack is struck. Doc moistens his lips with his tongue. There is a brown strip on his handkerchief when he wipes them. The open pages of Wyomin's notebook are as brown as the cover—he taps it on the seat and the dust drops off. But we are satisfied— we have almost reached our strip oasis.

The road pitches as it follows a winding and narrow course. It alternates between strips of loose gravel and solid-rock bumps which can be mighty hard on automobile tires. Halfway down we see an approaching car and hunt for a passing spot. The choice is not too good but it is the best available. We run our wheels up on the bank and wait for the other car. People strange to the country would approach with care and deliberation, but the hill climber, upon recognizing the Idaho license, evidently concludes that we have selected our position with the judgment of a native. His tires slip a little and throw a few rocks as he approaches, but he does not slacken speed. From where we sit, it appears that there are about six inches of solid road beyond the position of his outside tires, but to the mountain driver who knows exactly the location of his wheels on the road, six inches are all that is required. He passes with a sharp toot and a wave of the hand. I turn and see a puff of smoke from his cigarette as he leans more heavily on his accelerator.

Finally the road reaches the bottom and comes into a pleasant cluster of cottonwoods. From there on it continues down canyon for some miles, sometimes easily and sometimes barely competing with the river in the narrow places. This particular canyon is almost filled with trees. The little resort at Murphy Hot Springs probably provides the best fishing in southern Idaho. The fishing, and the hot springs which come out of the south canyon wall, and the fall hunting attract a regular stream of visitors.

We unpack and store our gear in the cabin we have rented and then move with our notebooks and material into the pleasant shade of the trees. Only those who have emerged from the hot desert and enter a strip oasis such as this can have an idea of the pleasure it brings. The dust has vanished; the heat is here, but it is clean and not unpleasant. The stream chatters cheerfully behind the cabin, the little hydrogenerator which furnishes the local electric power purrs like a contented tomcat. A cowboy rides by on a beautiful buckskin stallion. He might be going to a Hollywood studio, so striking is his getup. An afternoon thunderstorm may be due; we cannot see the sky over the mountains, but an occasional dimming of the sun indicates that clouds are beginning to form. The camp dog, a pleasant shepherd, calls and inspects us closely. The result is satisfactory, for she lies down and prepares to stay for a while.

The plant life around is a combination of grasses and herbs, separated a few feet away from the water by trees of which the peach-leaf willow seems to be the commonest kind. Beyond the grass and toward the canyon sides are the cottonwoods, clustered in some numbers and providing welcome shade.

The lower winds of the canyon are not like those above. We have noticed that when we are walking perhaps a couple of hundred feet up on the canyon wall and beyond the cottonwood tops, the breeze is hotter than below. We really find relief from the hot and searing wind of the desert when we are near the creek—or perhaps the surroundings relax us enough to give us that feeling. And why not?

In places where the stream bed is fairly level, the water makes a sound which might resemble the repetition of a minor note sounded over and over on the piano. Even the insects fly with a hum, not excluding the mosquitoes which candor makes me state can be rather annoying at times. Swallows fly back and forth, picking up insects which go to their almost certain destruction if they leave the shelter of the trees. And if they stay in the shrubbery they are not sure of

asylum, for never have I seen a place where the bird
life is more active. I mention the fact to Doc.

He begins to call them off—that crisp note is the
Wright flycatcher, one of the most characteristic birds
of the canyon. It is common and lives on foods not
to be found upon the sagebrush desert. It is a trim
bird, always cocking its head when looking for insects. While most of the birds of the sage desert are
seed eaters, the birds of the canyon bottoms are insect-
eating forms like yellow warblers, warbling vireos,
Wright flycatchers, robins, and russet-backed thrushes.
The trees usually harbor screech and horned, as well
as long-eared, owls. Dippers and kingfishers fly along
the creek. Garter snakes and toads, including the
northwestern, Woodhouse, and cricket tree toads, are
among the common amphibians.

Mammal life, too, is characteristic of the canyon.
Trade rats live along the walls, cottontail rabbits are
common, while jumping mice and meadow mice seek
the moist meadows and stream sides. Coyotes and
bobcats range a country which certainly must afford
them good hunting.

Life goes on peacefully here. The nearest railway
is miles away. The stage runs only twice a week. In
an emergency, a phone call will bring a plane to
buzz the ranch and wait for its passengers on the
plateau above, but the expense limits the use of this
system to emergencies only. The visitors come to
take life easy. A few fishermen follow the stream banks
with such success that we are constantly offered fish.

"Just right for a camp fryin' pan," says Wyomin'.
"You can leave their heads and tails on for handles
and you can eat them up one side of the backbone
and down the other, just like you take the kernels

off an ear of sweet corn, holdin' it in your hands."

Even the dogs seem to be taking it easy. They loll under the quiet trees.

The yellow warblers have been the only singers. As it clouds up more, they increase their tempo until the grove is full of their pleasant trill. Then peewees add their mournful little call as the storm threatens, and twice we hear the bubbling song of the house wren. At twilight we will see the nighthawks high-flying over the trees, while just above the treetops the broader winged poorwills can be told by their fluttery, mothlike flight. The poorwill is perhaps the most widely distributed bird in the Owyhee Desert. Doc says he has never passed an evening without hearing or seeing these birds.

We always think and speak of the extreme contrast; in shaded places we find clusters of roses, haws, and wild cherry which make a combination of the type the Texans call a "sticky thicket." A five-minute drive will take us above into the typical desert vegetation of sagebrush, rabbit brush, cheat grass, and the remains of a few spring-flowering annuals.

The odor of the canyon in daytime is slightly scented with the cottonwood trees, a faint touch of sage, and, if there is a cattle or horse ranch near by, with that previously mentioned and famed scent, Corral No. 5. I did not realize how greatly odors changed at the first touch of rain.

The small cloud which was building up has expanded and is now over us. The air has been calm up to now. A stiff breeze runs along the canyon, stirring up a little dust and humming through the trees. The new air smells strongly of moist sagebrush. Doc said it was because "the evaporation of the raindrops

from the sage has picked up some of the aromatic oils and evaporated them as well." This perfume driven ahead of the storm might be one answer to the old saying that horses can smell rain. We noticed that the horses we had been watching bounded off to the shelter of a grove of trees just before the storm started. The first drops came slowly and were followed by a rush of big ones which darkened the surface of the soil for only a few minutes before they dried up. The air now smells strongly of sage and cottonwood—quite a nice mixture. And from the groves come the soft odors of leaves, a fishlike fragrance from the river, and the bittersweet scent of the stagnant bottom pools.

This is a typical description of a portion of a strip oasis—typical, of course, except for the presence of this little resort which is outstripped in buildings and personnel by many a sheep ranch.

The first whites to visit these strips were unquestionably the trappers who overlooked no streams in their persistent and methodical search for beaver. Since, even in that time, beaver brought the trappers as much as four dollars a pelt, the successful trapper made wages which were greatly envied.

The beaver are no longer a part of the local economy, but the strip oasis is of the greatest importance in other ways. Most of the agriculture is based on these protected and well-watered spots. Nearly every stockman south of the Snake has a ranch in one of the canyons, for the protection and feeding of his stock. The home ranch usually consists of ranch house, one for the help, sheds, corrals, and, on sheep ranches, sheds and thatch-fenced corrals for lambing.

Stock raising would be almost impossible without

these canyons. Here is water, protection from the winter winds and blizzards. Here feed can be raised and stored to tide the band over the rough part of the winter. The area will support a more varied type of agriculture, but since so much is needed and its value so great in emergencies, hay is the principal crop. The fields are spotted by haystacks which are available when needed and left untouched as long as the pasture is sufficient.

The forage on the desert may be so sparse and scattered that a great many acres are required to furnish spring pasture for one cow; but, since there are many thousands of acres, the total contribution of these almost arid districts is considerable. It is well to remember, however, that the proper use of these acres is only made possible by the stability of these comparatively small canyon ranches, or strip oases, which can provide shelter and a certain supply of feed to carry the sheep and cattle when open-range forage is not available.

CHAPTER XVII

A Jack Just Stays Around

The early morning sun was a great disk above the horizon. The shadow of the moving car seemed to stretch out for a city block. We wore our light windbreakers because the air was cool. We had just climbed the last curve and reached the plateau above the Jarbidge River when we saw a number of black shapes some distance ahead on the highway. Morning desert light has a curious way of magnifying things so that a small animal appears large. These shapes loomed larger than a sheep, but they were not sheep; they were not built like mammals, and they moved about differently from sheep. We dropped into a little hollow and when we got high enough to see them again we were much closer. Keen-eyed Wyomin' spoke first.

"Eohippus, those things are eagles, golden eagles, and there's nine of them! This is goin' to make us look like liars when we tell about it. We better keep still except among friends. Nine eagles on an Idaho road. Who ever heard of it before?"

We were near enough now to see some animal carcasses as the birds got heavily into the air and rose slowly. An eagle has a wingspread of over six feet. Nine birds, each with over six feet of wingspread, made an imposing sight as they moved away. They were dark brown with greenish-yellow legs. Their wings were not narrow but appeared so in contrast with the length of their bodies.

"Nine of them," said Doc. "I never saw anything like it, and perhaps even our friends won't believe that we saw it today. It looks like three pairs and three young ones—I can see the light patches in the wing and at the base of the tail. They probably nest in the cliffs along the canyon, and they have come to the road to feed."

"I thought that the golden eagle always took its food alive," I said.

"One authority says that he has examined many nests," said Doc, "and never found any carrion, which, of course, is putrefying flesh, but he had no way of knowing whether a rabbit might have been badly wounded or nearly dead when it was taken."

"Roads are changin' some feedin' methods in Western States," said Wyomin'. "The long ears get on the road at night and they try to outrun the car, and if they don't make it, long ears stop travelin' for good. The night is cool and often birds and mammals start feedin'. Maybe there's still movement in the rabbit when the predators get on the job. Anyway, the meat's as fresh as when the predator does its own killin'. It might get in the habit of usin' this place to make an easy livin'."

Doc said, "It could be. We do know that some small flesh-eating animals have extended their range

to include highways where the auto kill is plentiful.
We know that ravens and crows feed on the roads.
It may be that hawks will eventually take advantage
of this regular night kill. It is extraordinarily large
in some districts."

That was the end of the talk about rabbits, but the
subject often came up again. We saw rabbits every
day around our camp, or from the car if we traveled.
The kinds we saw depended on our location. The
white-tailed jack sticks pretty much to the higher
slopes and, in our experience, is much less numerous
than the black-tailed, the common jack of the lower
altitudes. There are two smaller rabbits—the cottontail and the pygmy. The cottontail, of course, is known
over much of the United States both for the hunting
it furnishes and as a table delicacy. Many, and I am
one of them, think it better than chicken. The pygmy
rabbit is usually found in Owyhee in the tallest, dens-
est sagebrush; and the fact that it lives largely on
highly aromatic shrubs makes it much less desirable
for table purposes. Young jacks are eaten by some
people, but the older animals are not considered desirable, locally.

The lack of exact knowledge of local animals by
the residents is well illustrated by a story which Doc
tells of one of the inhabitants of the county. Doc
asked the rancher what kinds of rabbits were on his
ranch. He mentioned cottontails and pygmies, very
few blacktails, and then spoke of whitetails which he
saw only in summer, and of "snowshoe hares" which
visited the area only in winter. The latter two were
the same, of course, since the body of the whitetails
turns white in winter. The whitetails and the blacktails are really hares but are everywhere spoken of

as jack rabbits, or jacks. Audubon first used the name of "jack rabbit" in literature.

Because of their wide distribution and great numbers, the black-tailed jack rabbit is probably by far the most important rabbit in the country. It is usually this species that the traveling tourist sees and which has made the jack rabbit a well-known animal in the state. It dashes ahead of the automobile and bounds into the brush in the daytime. It appears in the glare of the headlights after dark, often confused by the light, and races madly ahead instead of making the leap to right or left which would take it to safety. Possibly it ultimately makes the abrupt change of direction, but the carcasses visible in the morning indicate that many have been killed by an overtaking car. Thousands die; many, many thousands remain. Night after night the performance is repeated—the engulfing light, the confused dash, the failure to deviate, and the disaster.

Wyomin' repeated a remark which one of his father's ranch hands had made about the black-tailed jack. "Pretty nigh all animals have some kind of a home; mebbe a burrow they dug or they found already dug. Mebbe it's a crack in the rock, or a cave—or it could be a hole in a tree. Whatever it is, it's a protection and a place where the young ones can be warm and comfortable. But a jack ain't that kind of a critter— it ain't got no home at all. It just stays around. Unless you call home a scratched-out place that a ground-nestin' bird wouldn't even use."

Wyomin' said, "Of course it's true. They scoop out a shallow depression under a shrub or in grass where it is kind of thick, and that's where they raise their young. They just stay around. I can understand how old Watty felt about it. He can't figure how any animal that can't fight or defend itself, and doesn't even have a tight livin' place, can exist and get along."

"You can't make judgments on such subjects off-hand," said Doc. "You have to figure the points in its favor and those against it. The way an animal holds its own depends on whether it brings to maturity more young than the total deaths in that period. Black-tailed jacks in Owyhee County aren't in as bad shape as your friend Watty thinks. Rabbits are probably better fitted to their environment than he has any idea of."

I remembered the havoc that one domestic rabbit had played with my garden one spring. It had escaped from a pen that a man had built to house the animal as a pet. Unlike most pampered pets, it did not voluntarily return to the pen from which it had escaped. My garden was the largest in the near-by neighborhood, so it concentrated on it. I would not have objected to supporting a dozen wild rabbits if they fed in one place that I could choose. But this rascal would not taste mature stuff; it preferred to run down a row of cabbage plants which I had just purchased for two dollars and neatly nip the plants into quite unworkable pieces. It clipped the leaves from sixty new strawberry plants and they all died. I planted peas four times before I could get enough to satisfy our modest family demands. As for carrots, I quit planting them when I found that the tops were regularly used for its salad or dessert.

I have no quarrel with wild animals. I give and take with the pheasants in the matter of sprouted bean plants and, by planting them twice as close as the authorities recommend, I strike a satisfactory balance.

The five or six California quail sample bits of many things, but they act like the gentle creatures they are. But this tame rabbit threatened to put me out of the gardening business, and I got mad. I tried to trap him, but he dodged the trap. Although he would come out on the front lawn and feed at dusk, his five-inch ears never stopped working and he was down the hill in a flash when the back doorknob clicked. I waited for him early in the morning. I could never move a foot without his knowing it; and away he would lope, not wildly, but gently and leisurely as if to indicate his total lack of respect for me. I am sure he will be back next spring to resume the contest. He has taught me that the rabbit is not always as gentle and trusting a character as the nursery books have represented him.

There is probably a substantial fraction of a million blacktails in Owyhee County. Possibly there are several times that number. Think of my lone domestic rabbit, innocent of outdoor life, and what he did to my garden. Think of the millions of jacks which "just stay around" in the wild. Normally they feed on the native shrubs and grasses, but when the population gets too great and they call on cultivated fields, one might as well try to stop the water rushing from a broken dam. They make trails into the grain as if tramped by cattle; before long, the whole patch is a trail and the grain has vanished.

This is not a discussion of the rabbit problem in general but merely an attempt to show how tremendous a factor they are in a country like Owyhee where the few green irrigated spots are surrounded by hundreds of acres populated by jacks. In some sections of the United States the rabbit is not only looked after

by the game department but is regarded with favor.
But in Owyhee the balance seems heavily against it.

What kind of an animal is this black-tailed jack?
It is about two feet long with ears six inches long
and with small front feet and powerfully muscled,
long rear legs. It has been said that the existence
of the jack is largely due to its acute sense of hearing and its great speed. If this is true, it is greatly
assisted by its build. Its legs propel it with a series
of long bounds. It takes the swiftest of dogs to equal
its speed, and so quickly does it twist and double that
a successful chase, except when surprise is involved,
is usually made only by two or more pursuing animals
which spread out enough to prevent any abrupt turns
to right or left. Its ears move and search in a way
that makes me think of a powerful searchlight as it
probes the air for possible trouble and the approach
of an enemy. They are huge, those ears. If those of
man were equally proportioned, his ears would be
a foot and a half in length. The animals weigh from
four and a half to eight pounds and are not small,
but so closely does the gray of their bodies blend
with the desert that they are most difficult to see.

Wyomin' proved to me how much constant practice
could improve a man's vision and ability to detect
things which the untrained man overlooked. Blacktails, like other jacks, have the habit of standing motionless while a passer-by is close. I never was able
to detect one in such a position, but Wyomin' constantly called my attention to big jacks which watched
us. Only their ears betrayed their interest and concern. When I asked Wyomin' how he managed so
consistently to find them, he said, "Don't look for a
jack. Look for motion. By and by it affects you like

the ring of a bell. You know these thick bush stems can't move. If there's motion, there's somethin' alive —and ten to one it's a jack."

He was nearly always right. We usually found that if we continued our pace, the jack did not move; but if we stopped or appreciably reduced our speed there was a huge flurry and the animal bounded off to stop a few yards away and look us over for a moment before resuming its departure.

Wyomin' showed me "forms," the name given to the shallow depression used for a nest. He seemed to have a feeling for them and often would go almost straight to a bush and find, as snug as you please, three or four young. We wondered if, when predators were much more plentiful, they had not located these forms without difficulty and disposed of a whole family in one visit. The litters run up to six, largely dependent on conditions of food, weather, and such factors. As far as we have been able to determine, there is only one brood a season in Owyhee.

Such an annual increase is not excessive in the animal world. On the contrary, the tremendous population which the blacktails often reach indicates that the mortality of these defenseless creatures is not as great as one might expect. Jacks are hardy. Their manner of living insures that.

The evidence in Owyhee shows that blacktails and other rabbits are subject to great cyclic variation. The population appears to increase year by year until, as one of the natives said, "There's a rabbit under every sagebrush." Then something happens and the number drops so low that for a while the sight of a jack rabbit is almost a rarity. The area affected is not necessarily large. These reductions appear to affect smaller sections so that at times there will be an excess of population in one valley and a shortage in another.

Doc has found no evidence that climate is the most important factor in these variations. Unquestionably, weather takes many of the young if a storm strikes at the critical time. Food and cover affect population, but not enough to be of importance in establishing these cycles. Here is a page from his notes:

Jack rabbits were extremely abundant. Sometimes the rabbits were so thick that I had the impression of driving through herds of them as one would drive through bands of sheep on the road. They were most numerous where the sage was sparsest, although they were absent from bare dune areas. Only a few were seen where the road was bordered by high and thick sagebrush. Usually the car would come upon them unawares and only 80 to 100 feet away, at which time they would sit bolt upright, often leap high in the air, and then bound off. They would seldom run down the road, but would turn directly into the sagebrush. Younger rabbits showed more confusion in such situations than the adults. One adult decided to run down the center of the road, instead of diving into the brush. This gave me an opportunity to check its speed. Pressed closely by the car, only about 20 feet behind, it maintained a pace of 50 miles per hour for ten seconds. In attempting to force it to a greater speed, I inadvertently caught up with and ran over the jack, thus ending the experiment. Fifty miles was probably the top speed.

Predation has been of considerable importance. Some hawks and owls, cougars, wildcats, and coyotes have preyed heavily upon both young and old blacktails. Figures on their kill, of course, do not exist but it is doubtless large. Unfortunately, man has had a private quarrel with the greatest predator, the coyote, because of its persistent killing of livestock, particularly sheep. In some places in Idaho it is said that the coyote is almost nonexistent and no factor at all as a predator. It is considerably to the advantage of the stockman, but much to the disadvantage of the grain grower and general farmer because it has relieved the pressure on the rabbits and on the small rodents which live on the desert and so heavily invade green fields and pastures. Now, certain ranchers are protesting the stringent control of the coyote on the ground that, although it is a predator on sheep and undesirable for that reason, its importance as a controller of the rabbits and small rodents makes the total balance in its favor.

Curiously enough, man, with all his ingenuity, has been able to do very little to control the blacktail effectively in Owyhee County or, in fact, anyplace else in range country. He has used poison but has found that the effect is only temporary and the expense too great. Trapping has caught many of the pests but the numbers seem unaffected. Great drives used to be held and thousands of animals were taken by forcing them into portable corrals where the bewildered creatures squalled like babies while men and boys with clubs slaughtered them by the thousands. I have often heard the pitiful cry of one wounded jack, and to hear a thousand at one time is an experience which I would not like.

One drastic method of control has been used in Australia, continental Europe, and Great Britain. This is a virus which, in its first use, proved so potent that its effect was appalling. Rabbits were not only reduced in numbers but almost exterminated. Stricken animals staggered about only to join the al-

ready dead. Australia was jubilant, for rabbit depre-
dation had pressed heavily on its economy and the
problem appeared to be solved. The rejoicing was
premature. Already, it is reported, life has refused
to be eliminated and a new strain, an immune strain
if you please, has appeared. It is quite probable that
the rabbit will continue to be a problem.

Running rabbits on horseback was for years a favorite sport, and many a rider has been thrown and a
horse injured when its leg dropped into a badger hole.
There has been much shining and shooting at night.
Lurking around a haystack and shooting the rabbits
as they came to feed was effective, but the animals
came so fast that the cost of shells was prohibitive
when cash was at a premium. Nowadays, a favorite
sport is shooting rabbits at night from an automobile.
The hunters figure they are performing a public
service.

"I tried that once," said Doc. "One late afternoon
two friends came down from Emmett and took me
to the Murphy area to look for jack rabbits and
kangaroo rats. The evening, however, was rather
windy and we didn't see too many animals. One of
the men said the rabbits didn't like to come out on
windy nights as the wind prevented them from hearing equally well from all directions. Those we did
see had their ears laid back and were much more
wary than usual. They would not hold well when
spotted in the light. We got about a dozen and a half."

Experience seems to show that the best way of keeping rabbits out of a field is with a rabbit-proof fence,
and that frequently fails. There are many hundreds
of miles of it in Australia where rabbits have been
so great a pest that some land has had to be aban-

doned. There the fence must provide for protection underground, for the English rabbit, imported to help the ranchers, has become the greatest of all mammal pests in Australia, and doubly so because it is a burrower.

On the economic side, few or no benefits are derived from the blacktail. Doc sums it up in this way: "The rabbits, in providing much meat for the large hawks and owls, take the pressure off the domestic poultry and young lambs and must be counted as of some value. They afford some sport to hunters. As far as I can determine, they are not trapped in Owyhee County nor are they eaten by the residents. This is not true of some sections of the United States where rabbit fur is regularly traded in and the meat is sold in the markets. The *Encyclopaedia Britannica* mentions that in one year 70,000,000 rabbit skins were exported by Australia."

The debits on the economic side make a rather black showing. Where they are numerous in timbered areas they destroy many small trees, cutting off their tender tops each year until the tree either succumbs or, if overlooked for a season, finally puts up a top out of reach of the pest.

The cost of blacktails to the ranchers is enormous. The rabbits are usually so numerous that the carrying capacity of the range is greatly reduced and some irrigated fields during the peak of the cycles are completely denuded. Much of the damage done is in territory regularly grazed by the domestic animals so that the damage is not readily apparent, but it is there nevertheless.

"Wyomin'," Doc asked, "you know the jack-rabbit problem from the standpoint of the rancher and stockman. What does the man in the country think of jacks?"

The answer was prompt. "Not much. They wouldn't mind a few, but there's too many of them. They wouldn't think so bad of them if they would stick to the range, but they bother irrigated fields and gardens. They're mighty unpopular right now. One farmers' organization actually has gone on record favorin' the removal of some of the pressure on coyotes because they take so many rabbits. Ranchers don't think much of coyotes, but apparently some think they destroy enough jacks to offset the injurious things they do."

CHAPTER XVIII

Desert Mountains

We were talking of mining days as we drove toward the Silver City Range. The car climbed steadily on roads which city drivers would have thought dusty and rough but which to us, accustomed to the desert by-roads, seemed as satisfactory as town pavements. From time to time we stopped to view the panorama below us—enormous desert flats, indistinct in the distance, and rimmed by dim mountains.

"I don't understand how so many people could live on a desert mountain," I said. "It would be like running a herd of cattle on a rock pile. Think of the fuel and water problem."

"There was a naturalist named Merriam who was one of the first men to explain why and how that could be done," said Doc. "He observed that plant and animal life were much affected by temperature. Because elevation greatly affects temperature, there's a great difference in the desert life at 3,500 feet and the mountain life at 5,000 to 8,000 feet. Also, the

Silver City Mountains are regular storm breeders, and their thunderstorms give the area moisture which seldom directly reaches the desert below. In other words, elevation affects temperature, precipitation, growing season, water supply, and thus plants and animals. You'll see some remarkable changes by the time we reach Silver City."

We climbed almost continuously through little valleys, on ridge tops and along narrow gouges bulldozed in the hillsides. Dry washes far below wandered through the bare and desolate valleys. The scene shifted from bleak slopes to distant views of the desert and, rarely, a brief glimpse of the irrigated sections near the Snake River. We saw few cattle or sheep along these bleak miles; both water and feed were too scarce, except in spring. We had started early, but the sun was hot and where the light breeze did not reach us we were quite uncomfortable.

Doc talked of these mountains which rose out of the thousands of square miles of Owyhee County, and about the important part they had played in the history of the area. Their mines had produced some forty million dollars' worth of precious metals. They had made possible the settlement and development of the stock range which looks to the mountains for its water supply. And yet, percentage-wise, they constitute a small portion of the county. From a standpoint of latitude and longitude they are connected with and surrounded by the deserts, but the altitude and consequent conditions of their upper levels have completely removed them from those found on the desert. They really form what might be called huge vertical oases. The only moisture below them is along the few streams, the various water holes, dune lakes, and sources of water described elsewhere.

There was no sign of this promised land as we climbed steadily. The dust was just as deep—and perhaps deeper in the protected washes—than in the lake-bed country. The vegetation appeared scantier. The shrubs seemed smaller than those below. The grass had been well cleaned out. No greenness separated it from the brown of the lower lands.

Wyomin' checked the outlook on both sides of the car and then jokingly said, "Altitude hasn't been gettin' in any of its licks so far, Doc. It don't look like a fenced pasture yet. In fact, it seems like more is bein' chomped off than can grow. And we must be gettin' pretty high, too."

Doc just smiled and said nothing. More dust blanketed the trailer and shut off the view to the rear. We climbed a steep sidehill grade, bumped over a small flat, and started up a little canyon. Then he spoke. "You asked for a change, Wyomin'. Well, here it is." The side walls narrowed and the road began to follow a small creek in a bottom where the green of grass was visible and a few aspens trembled in the breeze. "We're getting into a new kind of country now."

We did see a change. The little creek actually bubbled and gurgled in a few spots. More blooming roadside plants appeared, their blue and yellow flowers contrasting pleasantly with the dirt floor. The aspens reached a little higher. We climbed and twisted through changing vegetation which sometimes arched the road. Pentstemons brightened the rock walls with the pink of their plentiful blooms. Magpies flew in and out of the trees and squawked noisily.

Juniper trees occupied favorable locations; the air was filled with the pleasantly spicy odor of their heated vegetation. We were leaving the desert below and, as Doc had predicted, we were surprised at the change.

The rough road made driving slow but, with care, we kept on a fairly bumpless course which eventually brought us to an open spot where the road disappeared down a drop. We got out of the car. We had climbed steadily for some time but we found that the descent on the other side was even more precipitous and winding. We could see the water of a stream in a valley half a mile below.

"It's Jordan Creek which runs through Silver City," said Doc. "We're less than three miles from town. This is New York Summit and an important point. It's the last pass that stood between the miners and the El Dorado of their dreams."

We looked the country over. They had to get the ore up this steep rise when they hauled to Salt Lake City. We could still see the deep ruts made by the loaded wagons. They must have had extra teams here to help negotiate the steep grades. There was no noise now but, at one time, the hills echoed with the cries of the teamsters and the crack of their rawhide whips as the horses leaned into their collars and toiled inch by inch up the rocky steepness. We realized how much hauling there must have been, for mining means tonnage.

"I apologize for kiddin' about the lack of change," said Wyomin'. "It was slow comin', but when it changed it did it pronto. And, Eohippus, look at the trees. And there's some alpine firs. And the flowers —they make a high-grade garden. No lack of water and no blow sand up here."

A profusion of especially pleasing bloom covered the hills on either side of the narrow pass. I suppose it was nothing extraordinary, but its freshness stood out against the desert we had left. We saw gray Phacelia with its attractive blue flowers; a blue lupine not known to us; a tawny mustard which bore light yellow blooms; a coil-pod vetch with yellow blossoms darker than those of the mustard. We noted black elderberry, narrow-leaved brome grass, and the additional yellows provided by the California gromwell and the cushion buckwheat. Could the desert be only a few miles away from this place?

"It's a distinctive patch," said Doc. "We're seeing different things because we're in a different life zone. Zone boundaries aren't like a fence or road with one kind on one side and other species beyond, but they do differ so that each condition has its characteristic list."

Across Jordan Creek rose the sky line of eight-thousand-foot mountain crests with steep and rocky flanks sparsely tree-covered, and with much snow still remaining in protected spots under the peaks. Near the summit in one place, acres of stripped ground and a dump indicated the failure of a recent attempt by one of the big contracting companies to profitably mine low-grade ores with modern low-cost methods. The workings had been deserted.

"There's a bigger difference than I thought I'd see," said Wyomin'. "Look at that pair of hairy woodpeckers in the tree. I haven't seen any like them below."

"Almost everything will be different," said Doc. "There are beavers just down the hill. If you see chipmunks, they won't be the subspecies you see on

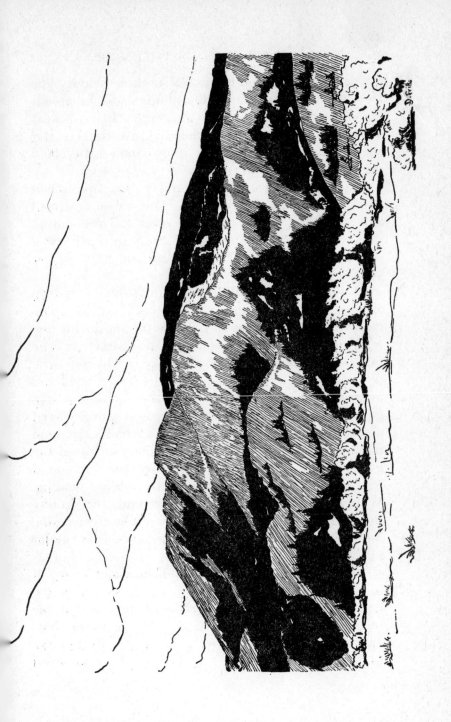

the desert. You'll find hawks unlike those below. The trees won't be the same. The flowers will be almost entirely different. If a man who knows Idaho botany were dumped out here in the dark, he could pretty well determine the elevation just as soon as he could see the plants around him."

We started down the hill and passed the beaver dam which Doc had mentioned. The stream was small and steep; the markings of the trees and the stumps showed where the animals had been working. Substantial dams slowed up the stream and held smaller ponds.

At the foot of the hill we again stopped to look around. A man passing on horseback pulled up to talk with us. We spoke of the country and its history.

"You're in quite a historic spot," he observed. "The first legal hanging in Silver City occurred right here. A mule skinner was nabbed after he had robbed and killed a man. He tried to bury the corpse but digging was hard, so one of the boots wasn't quite covered and somebody found the body. They had a trial and my father drove by just after they had convicted the robber. They throwed a rope over the limb of a tree that used to be about where you're standing. When the robber saw my dad he said, 'Ed, you're the only man I know around here. They're hanging me and I want you to kick the box out from under me.' So he did."

The rider talked of road conditions and trails, of livestock and game. When he left, it was with the true optimism of the pioneer—a prediction that the region wasn't exhausted yet, and that some of these days there would be another strike which would wake up the whole country. I looked at the abandoned

workings during the day and was not so sure. But
there is a chance that the new mineral-detecting devices may locate materials, unknown half a century
ago, but in great demand today.

We drove a short mile up sparkling little Jordan
Creek, where Chinamen once had hand-sifted the
gravel bars in their search for gold. The hills, which
we had been told were quite thickly covered with
trees at one time, had many patches of new growth.

"They stopped mining just before the wood supply
was exhausted," said Doc. "They had it almost cut
out. I suppose that costs of fuel and mine timber
must have constantly increased. But this was a pretty
good life zone to pick for mining—comfortable climate, plenty of water and fuel, which lasted as long as
the ore."

We crossed the bridge and entered what was left of
the town. Practically all residences had been burned
or dismantled. Few of the buildings on the main
streets were in any kind of repair. The frame hotel
which had sheltered such men as "Andy" Mellon still
stood, but it was locked. Brick walls of former substantial edifices had crumbled or been removed. The
old dumps indicated onetime activity, as did broken
and rusty pieces of equipment. We didn't need to
look at them. A glance at the prospect-spotted hills
which had yielded millions, together with a play of
the imagination, would better bring back the glories
of the district's golden youth than the sight of worn-
out buildings and empty streets.

We turned up a side road and passed War Eagle
Summit and along the ridge road to Cinnabar Summit, where we had a tough time getting up the last
hundred yards because the high elevation and heat

caused vapor lock in the carburetor. We thought we
would find snowdrifts available for a water supply,
but spent the next four hours looking for them on
neighboring ridges. We wanted three things: water,
trees for shade, and a view. We finally spotted a
saddle next to a grove of alpine firs only a few yards
from an ice-cold spring. I thought it an ideal spot.
But we found differently when we checked the surroundings. We noticed that the whole saddle was
cut to a powdery dust by elk and deer tracks and
we found a salt lick close by.

"This place won't do," said Doc. "After dark it
will be as active as a political convention. If we camp
here and keep those animals from getting at that
salt lick and spring they'll set up a bawling that will
outdo a rally for a favorite candidate. We'll get no
sleep at all. Let's hunt elsewhere."

We picked a spot a little distance away on a projecting bluff near a cliff. We would be more exposed
to wind and we would have to go after water, but
it was better than listening all night to the protests
of indignant deer and elk.

When we went to the spring for water, we stopped
to talk to a packer who had set up camp in the saddle.
He had six pack mules and a couple of riding horses.
The herder was with the band. We watched as the
man prepared his meal. He was baking sourdough
bread in an iron camp stove which had a small oven
on the right side. The rest of the meal was a mulligan stew in a Dutch oven. He had dug a hole in
the ground, filled it with sagebrush, and let it burn
down. Then he placed the oven in the hole and
piled hot embers and earth over it. He said it would
take an hour to cool and the mulligan would be done.

I had often seen them bake this way; all done with a fire hole and Dutch oven.

After supper we counted eighteen deer in the chaparral below us. The next day we looked for other game. The deer and the elk appear to feed in the open in the early morning, after which they "brush up" in the trees during the day, coming out to feed again in the evening. They particularly like the Ceanothus brush which grows on otherwise barren hillsides.

The next day we walked several miles along the ridge, high enough so we could see the whole pattern of the county. To the south lies the great interior basin in which Triangle is located. Southwest of this rises the South Mountain Range from which a heavily eroded and juniper-covered elevated area extends eastward and forms the southern boundary of the above basin, which Doc calls the Owyhee Highlands. South of this latter is a large area which Doc calls the Breaks of the Owyhee. It is strongly croded and has juniper patches on the lee side of the knolls where the drainage is down into the Owyhee River. South of this drainage system, the Owyhee Plateau, grass and sage covered, stretches unbroken to the various mountain ranges of northern Nevada. To the west, it meets the Santa Rosa Mountains of Nevada and the Blue Creek Mountains of Oregon. To the east, the high plateau is broken by an escarpment just west of the Grasmere-Riddle area. East of where we stood lies a rolling and dissected intermediate plateau and, farther east, the Bruneau Desert. On the Oregon line, a low saddle separates the South Mountain Range from the Parsnip Mountains in Oregon. The Silver City Range is cut off from the Ruby Mountains by the gorge of Castle Creek.

"Early settlers had a hard time gettin' around in a country like this," said Wyomin'. "And another thing seems strange; wherever you look, everythin' is dry and baked below. Usually it is the low places that are wet. But around where we're sittin', way up above those places, we see streams and snowbanks and trees."

We also found that it could rain handily where we were. While we walked back to the camp a mass of thunderheads came in from the west and we got into the car just as we were struck by a brief mountain storm. Strong wind, frequent gushes of rain with terrific lightning for twenty minutes, hailstones of pigeon-egg size for part of the time, so that the car roof rattled like a snare drum, and the ridges were whitened. We hurriedly got supper together after the main storm and it was fortunate we did, for a lesser one followed after we had finished. Later in the evening it cleared and, to celebrate, we toasted wieners.

The next evening a band of sheep passed camp, bound for the shipping corral just below War Eagle Saddle. The herder came panting up the steep slope after he had driven the strays ahead. He had two dogs and carried a straight staff and was a young fellow, obviously a recent importation, for the American-bred Basque youth rarely goes into herding.

Doc said, "Good evening."

Basque: "Hello, no English, un poke." I suppose he meant by this, idiomatically, *"un poco de Inglés,"* in Spanish.

Doc: "You have a lot of sheep."

"Bueno. Deer? You see *muy* deer." Referring with a hand wave down the hill where there were about two dozen.

"Yes, there are a lot of deer down there."

"*Bueno.*"

Doc: "You work for Quintana? He's got a lot of sheep around here."

"*Si, muy* sheep."

"You are working late tonight."

"*Bueno. Si.* What you do here?"

Doc: "Just walking and looking at country."

Basque: "Just walking? Sonabeech, you make good sheepherder." And with a wave of his hand he walked slowly after his sheep.

The alpine grove in which we were camped is an isolated one, overlooking upper Boulder Creek Canyon. There must be about a hundred alpine firs in the grove, most of them thirty to forty feet in height and more or less scrubby in form.

The usual alpine birds for the region are present, but the alpine and montane mammals of other districts are missing because they cannot pass the desert barriers which surround the mountains. For that reason scientists are almost certain that the mountains were uplifted after the country became desert. Mammals that are common in other main mountain masses but are not found here are the black bear, red squirrel, flying squirrel, yellow pine chipmunk, water shrew, red-backed mouse, big-footed meadow mouse, and possibly some others. But the desert is no barrier to flying creatures. We saw such birds as the prairie falcon, raven, Clark's nutcracker, fox sparrow, white-crowned sparrow, mourning dove, golden eagle, screech owl, sparrow hawk, horned lark, and many others.

We talked about the great difference that these few thousand feet of elevation could make in the climate and characteristics of a place. A thirty-mile drive and an hour's time would take us to that life zone where the principal creatures were the jack rabbits, the lizards, the kangaroo rats, and the ground squirrels. As nocturnal creatures, they were just about to begin their evening activity. They would soon feed in the sand and the sage where the vegetation was gray and the day temperature over a hundred. But here we were near snow which fed the creeks, and near thunderstorms which briefly spread hail and rain, and furnished moisture for the many springs. No sufficiency below, no lack here—from the human standpoint. As I went to sleep that night, I thought of the wonderful efficiency of the great adjustment which populated every area in every altitude with forms of life suited to it and seeking it in preference to all other places.

CHAPTER XIX

Citellus

Every time I see Citellus, the ground squirrel, I think of a remark made by a philosophical hired hand whom we met. "No matter how little and close to nothing a thing is, if you get enough of 'em, they're bound to amount to a lot."

As I looked about on one of our June desert trips, this seemed particularly applicable to these small rodents. We saw them everywhere. Young and old, active and fat, they scampered over the ground in their characteristic rush for the next bit of cover.

In spite of their number, they appeared of no particular importance. They were but tiny dwellers in a tremendous acreage. How could they affect these miles that stretched before us? How could they be anything but insignificant, inoffensive, and harmless? But I knew that their impact on human economy was tremendous. I mentioned it to Doc.

"It's easy to see why," he said. "They are principally vegetation eaters and, if they are plentiful enough in areas where they compete with man for the products of the field and range, there's bound to be trouble. And yet their eating is of importance to other animals."

"What do you mean by that?" asked Wyomin'.

"The ground squirrels are a big factor in the food chains. They eat vegetation and get fat. The carnivores capture and eat them. The ground squirrel furnishes a considerable part of the food of some of the owls, hawks, and desert mammals."

"We ought to give it a little credit for that," said Wyomin'.

"Man doesn't think so. He isn't particularly interested in seeing plenty of food for coyotes, except where it keeps the animals away from his sheep and chickens. There's another thing against Citellus that doesn't make man particularly happy. The ground squirrels are hosts for carriers of spotted fever, tularemia, bubonic plague, and possibly other diseases. I can't say I enjoy taking shots for spotted fever before making these trips each spring. I get a mighty disagreeable reaction. So, altogether, Citellus is not too popular."

That is a preliminary summary of Citellus, the little burrowing rodent which exists in such numbers in the West. It's not too favorable, I admit, but nevertheless there is much of interest to be learned about ground squirrels. Almost every traveler in western country sees them. Their range covers parts of Europe, Asia, and of western and central North America. In general they are neat, busy little creatures, with quick, pert movements which attract sympathetic attention. Doc has always considered them an esthetic part of the landscape. There are five species in the county, including the Belding ground squirrel, the commonest in the area; the Richardson, which is the rarest; the Townsend, an inhabitant of the lower areas and once used by the Indians for food; the golden-mantled, a dweller in the higher elevations; and the white-tail antelope squirrel, which occurs in the northern part of the county.

All of these ground squirrels are diurnal, retiring to their burrows before dark, and the most active in early morning and late afternoon. These habits make them familiar to people who may never see other animals which are as numerous, but which have nocturnal habits. Because they are ground dwellers, they are almost never found in trees and, when they visit shrubs and bushes, they confine themselves to low levels. They often sit upright on their haunches when they wish to look around, and, like tree squirrels, they move rapidly when alarmed, stopping only when they have reached what they consider a safe place.

When we approach a sidehill with a grassy or herbaceous patch close below it, we are almost sure to find ground squirrel colonies, for they prefer to locate where the excavated earth is easily disposed of. Burrows are usually built in the most rock-free earth of the area. They particularly like a site near a grassy meadow along a creek. Usually we can detect the main nest by a mound of earth and by a larger entrance than those used only for quick retreat. Often we find the retreat entrances in or along the hard-baked surface of a graded road, probably because the animals spend much time feeding in grassy patches on the margins.

Burrows we have examined often have their entrance somewhat hidden by a bush or other form of plant growth. The animals build close together and often over huge areas, resulting in fantastically high populations which feed heavily on the native and cultivated crops.

The burrow entrance leads into a tunnel of some length, with chambers for the young and for storage. There may be short escape passages, drainage holes, and separate compartments for estivation or hibernation. There is nothing particularly complicated about these burrows, but to compare them with the rough nest (form) of the jack rabbits would be like comparing a modern house with the tepee of a Plains Indian.

Perhaps the rough form or nest of the jack rabbit provides a suitable place for the birth and early maintenance of its young. Certainly it would not do for the ground squirrel, which has uniquely adapted itself to its environment. For among the ground squirrels we have some species which spend up to 75 per cent of their time in dormancy. This condition is a means of meeting its environmental demands as is shown by the fact that some species, favorably situated, do not estivate or hibernate at all. It is in sections where the rains are confined to winter and where drought marks the short growing season that dormancy is carried to the extreme. The ground squirrels appear at a favorable time in spring and, having raised their family and put themselves in condition for a long sleep, they retire when drought and heat make living difficult.

We have watched them on the desert. In early February the fields and hollows are bare. Then in late February or early March the land fairly teems with ground squirrels. The sleep is over. About five

months of activity begins. Everywhere we look we
see ground squirrels, feeding, mating, fighting, going
about the business of their lives. They gorge themselves with available roots, flowers, and other plant
parts, digging bulbs and gleaning seeds, raiding any
near-by fields, attacking the vegetables. Small green
fields in large dry areas appear to suffer most. Some
which we have passed lose part of their green daily
as the margins take on the brownness of the surrounding desert. Strip after strip of grain or alfalfa disappears when the hungry hordes swarm at the feast.
If desert conditions are particularly dry, the whole
field may be taken.

Doc said there is a world of material for those
who want information about these industrious rodents.
They have been watched in the field and in captivity
under conditions which closely approach those of the
open. Many details of their life histories have been
well documented. You can read such things as how
far the animals range when feeding, what species store
food, what kind of food is stored, and when it is eaten.
Some species are partly carnivorous, some stick largely
to a vegetable diet. A regular calendar of their life
is available.

The males awake from their winter dormancy and
appear just as food becomes available. They are followed in a few days by the female, and mating takes
place almost immediately. There is enough fat re-
tained for energy purposes so that the arduous duty of
producing and maintaining a family may be carried on
properly. The young appear and the mature animals
lose weight for a short time until vegetation is plentiful, after which they accumulate a supply of fat which
will serve during the period of scarcity. Daily intake

has been variously estimated as from 15 to 35 per cent of the weight of the squirrel. Accumulation of fat, so abhorred by most human animals, appears to be the sole aim of the squirrel. The fat must carry the animal through the winter and start the new season as well. The ground squirrels become harvesters who appear on the scene only for the harvest bounty and disappear when the bounty is exhausted. Few species of Citellus make any concerted attempt at storage, although supplies are occasionally found in hibernating chambers.

They do not need direct water sources as do so many animals. They may obtain the necessary moisture from the food they eat, and, when the food becomes so dry that it no longer furnishes that moisture, they enter their hibernating chambers and leave the problem of active fall and winter existence to other animals.

Their development is concentrated. In approximately four months the young must suckle, be weaned, open eyes which are sealed for three weeks, gather a living with enough efficiency to put on the necessary store of fat, and construct a hibernating burrow to which they may retire for the fall and winter months. In spring they must emerge in good enough physical condition to mate and reproduce and begin the new cycle of fat accumulation.

I asked Doc how they got the information on hibernation. "It must have been a hard job," I suggested.

"It surely was. Dr. W. T. Shaw and his assistants excavated like a bunch of sewer diggers to investigate the hibernation of the Columbian ground squirrel. He marked the burrows during the active season, then excavated them in winter. At the end of four

years' study, he knew that the animals slept sitting up and rolled in a tight ball so that the head rested on the abdomen. He found that they constructed a regular hibernating compartment, originally connected with the summer main burrow but plugged off —it consisted of a snug sphere about nine inches in diameter and connected with an exit shaft and often with another tube used for drainage. The hibernating cell has dry dust on the bottom to protect the animal from moisture and is lined with nest material which just leaves room for the animal inside."

"That was certainly a discovery," I remarked.

"Wasn't it?" said Doc. "It wasn't a quick and easy one. It required much investigation. The pictures they secured were remarkable. Since then, other information has been accumulating slowly, until we know much about the life histories of all the ground squirrels. Their range has been worked out so that the average state animal book has maps showing the territory in which each species is found. Dr. Shaw and Mr. Theo. Scheffer have done lots of work in this field.

"There's much public interest in ground squirrels," said Doc. "I think it's because the animals are so widely spread out. People write us about all sorts of things they think are curious."

"What kind of things, Doc?"

"One man writes that ground squirrels continually swim an irrigating ditch to get at grain planted in his orchard. A grad from the agricultural college tells of the many nests he has ploughed up in one day—he thought the whole field was honeycombed with them. Another tells of a domestic cat which has brought in over two hundred dead animals. A student mails in notes of early and late records of animals he had taken in traps. Another described a new system of poisoning he thought was effective. Some of the information is worth while, some is useless; but the point is that the ground squirrel is a well-known animal and one which country people watch."

"They do well to watch them," said Wyomin'. "Breed, sleep, and eat seems to be the program of most wildlife, but these fellows are specialists. A single pair can produce enough young so that six or eight mouths are foragin' as soon as the young can get around. It may make for fulfillment of the destiny of the ground squirrel, but it's mighty wearin' on the rancher who sees his crop cut down to the disappearin' point. Maybe spectators can look at it calmly, but it's different when your pocketbook is tied up with the problem."

Ranchers have nothing good to say about ground squirrels. The pocket gopher, previously mentioned, may do as much, or more, harm, but the daylight and above-ground depredations of the ground squirrel so thoroughly advertise it that it is regarded as the greatest of rodent pests.

Certainly little good can be attributed to them. They eat insects such as grasshoppers and crickets, and it is quite possible that many are eaten before they have begun to multiply and do damage. But it is doubtful if their insect consumption is heavy enough to make for any kind of control. Their burrowing and earthworking tends to increase the arability of the soil, but the total effect is not great.

The harm they do unquestionably overshadows the good. There is the interference with physical features of the land: such things as slides caused by the mining of easily eroded soils; the burrowing which dries out the field and thus reduces the crop; the puncturing of irrigating ditches so that precious water is lost or parts of valuable fields flooded. But these losses are minor.

The real damage lies in the reduction or total destruction of vegetation. This might seem of little importance on the less productive parts of Owyhee, However, a desert is not a sterile place, as so many people think. It is an area of deficient rainfall, but it will support vegetation adapted to it. There are few places on the desert which will not produce some feed for stock, even if the amount produced is small and available only for spring range. The overrunning of such areas by rodents considerably reduces the spring forage which would otherwise be available. The ground squirrels take over areas so readily and maintain themselves so easily that they constitute a growing menace. They build up their colonies to the carrying capacity of the area. The old burrows are occupied year after year, and the young ones build new ones until the place is overrun.

The result is the decimating or destruction of crops in many cases, because the squirrels will invade everything but heavily irrigated fields. Especially harmful is the taking of young plants, for this often seriously affects production. In their search for moisture, they pull down and cut the juicy nodes of grains and grasses, discarding the greater part of the plant but completely ruining it. Some experts have estimated that twenty to twenty-five ground squirrels will eat as much as one sheep. The depredations of a whole colony are, therefore, of considerable importance.

Estimates of crop damage are not based on the prejudiced reports of disgruntled grain growers, but on tests made by competent observers and in controlled plots where the feeding of the animals can be constantly observed. Their enormous appetites enable them to consume several hundred wheat stems a day, or its equivalent in other vegetation. Such figures reveal their standing as potential enemies of crops.

Doc thinks that though control appears easy, the number of animals and the vast acreage involved complicate matters. Natural control may have been quite effective at one time, for there are many predators —coyotes, skunks, weasels, badgers, foxes, hawks, owls, and others. We used to see coyotes hunting in the Pilchuck meadows, but coyotes have been poisoned so continuously that they have lost their importance as a predator in Owyhee. Owls, mostly night feeders, affect the squirrels but little. Badgers hunt them successfully, as can be seen in places where they have been digging. Predation by snakes must be considerable, although it can only be conjectured. Even if predation is extensive, the number of squirrels remaining indicates that predators are not effectively controlling the situation.

This may be partially because the number of ground squirrels has been greatly increased by the extension of agriculture. The addition of man's attempts at control has apparently not improved the situation. Trapping and shooting are helpful only in small areas. Gassing is expensive and slow work. Poisoning has been effective where properly applied, but little has been done except on irrigated ranches where the acreage yield is great enough to justify it. The government has spent hundreds of thousands of dollars on various programs and as much more on research, but apparently the day is far off when a traveler through Owyhee in late spring will fail to see thousands of ground squirrels as they go busily about their work of converting valuable crops and range grass into the flesh required to maintain them through a long winter of sleep and the hectic entrance into the work of raising another family.

CHAPTER XX

Skeletons

We were on the plateau above the canyon. **Black** clouds hung low, but the setting sun illuminated their undersides and lit up the whole area with a strange, half-luminous light. Nothing looked natural; the top of the hills rose out of queer back lighting which made them soft and drippy; the sagebrush lost its briskness and stood limp and gummy-looking; the stones on the ground were without distinct outline and merged with their background. I had never seen a time when inanimate things were so modified by lighting conditions. The animals were affected also. The jacks we saw did not look like those of the bright sunlight; these, some young and some old, might have been ghost rabbits. They seemed to jump and run with a lightness unnatural in rabbits, and they lacked the solid reality of those seen on clear evenings. Who knows that they were not strangers? We did not get close enough to swear that they were merely ordinary rabbits transformed by this unusual sunset. The surroundings did nothing to build up a feeling of reality toward them. For here and there over the ground lay jack-rabbit skeletons and bones. Now, one seldom sees skeletons and bones of smaller animals because they are so fragile and small that they are broken by the weight of snow, the trampling by other animals, and some are torn apart by the force of the stiffer desert winds. The bones of some large animals last for years, possibly close to a century, if exposed in advantageous conditions on the desert soil. The bones of the smallest would hardly withstand the pelting of storm-driven rain. Jack rabbits are of an intermediate size, but their skeletons were not often seen in numbers by us before that evening. Perhaps hunters had come here often.

"It's a strange sight in this light; almost eerie," said Doc. "It looks like some sort of picture of the passing of time and the coming of death. There are the living ones, or representatives of the living ones, dancing about at sunset, and all around them are skeletons on the ground. The living will join the bones on the desert in another year or so."

"It's strange," I said, "but the sight reminds me of a picture I saw in one of the travel magazines where, in the 'bone room' at the monastery on Mount Sinai, several young monks were looking at skulls and bones of centuries of their predecessors. Ground was not available for permanent burial, so, after a few years, the bones were dug up and added to the tremendous stack in the bone room. In due time, the bones of these young spectators would join them."

We continued to watch as the sun went down and the sky grew black. The jack rabbits had vanished down a swale and only the skeletons remained. We resumed the subject as we left camp the next morning.

"One thing is certainly different on the desert than on the mountains of western Washington," said Doc. "The deserts do not hide their dead. You never see a sight like that in the Cascades."

Doc pointed to the skeleton of an animal. The bones were large and in their position on a slight eminence, framed by the sky, they looked enormous. Their whiteness contrasted vividly with the darkness of the sand beneath so that it dominated the area. It was just one of the range cattle whose kind were scattered about, but it looked unnatural. I had the feeling that I was looking at a skeleton which had lain there for many, many years. Doc added, "That's a common sight in this country, as you both know; you will see several every day you drive."

"Now you speak of it, there are a lot of them," said Wyomin'. "I think it's because they last so long. Each new one adds to the collection. I suppose that twenty years from now that frame will be lyin' there in about the same condition it is now. Certainly, it can't bleach any more."

"That's why I was comparing this desert with the Washington mountain country," said Doc. "When an animal passes out there, it may never be seen. It's covered by vegetation right away. It decomposes quickly. In a short time, it's a part of the soil. But in Owyhee, skeletons last."

"When I was on the ranch," said Wyomin', "I used to try and figure out what finished the critters off. Sometimes it's starvation or poison, but often it's accident. Let's take a look at this animal."

We walked over to the skeleton. There were many

things that could happen to stock. Disease, poisoning, bloat, miring, a broken leg, even remote causes
such as fire on the range, starvation under extreme
storm conditions, or lightning. Coyotes had brought
down many a weakened cow, and in the early days
wolves were so bad that experts had said that they
would prevent the West from ever being a good stock
country.

Wyomin' surveyed the scene carefully. Doc and I
watched as this practical man of the plains drew on
his experience for an explanation. He stopped at the
right front leg. He pointed to the leg bone. "Look
at that; this is badger country, and the poor critter
cracked the bone in a badger hole and was finished.
It wasn't exactly a natural death, but no predator
got it, although one might have stampeded the animal
and caused it to get into the hole."

As I pictured the scene, I concluded it wasn't a
pleasant death. One slip had changed a strong, healthy
animal into a helpless and doomed cripple. The animal could not leave the scene of the accident, but
lay down in the one place while sunsets faded, cold
nights passed, and the sun brought heat and drought.
No water, no relief, only pain and starvation. I did
not like to think of the number of days that might
have passed before death came. But it made me realize
how cruel the desert can be to a badly injured animal.

As the weeks passed, we conducted a regular side
course in desert demise until, superficially at least,
we had exhausted many of the possibilities. We examined skeletons and tried to see if our conclusions
checked.

We could not always be certain. The frame of
a cow near a coyote skeleton did not mean necessarily

that there had been some kind of a battle in which
two participants had perished. Usually the cow had
died and cattlemen had set traps around the carcass
and had captured one of the visitors which they knew
would surely be attracted. Coyotes were trap wise
and suspicious, and a man had to be clever to out-
wit them. A large animal made a good place for a
trap set, as the presence of so much meat seemed to
make the predators less wary.

Scattered bones usually meant that animals had
fed on the carcasses, although skeletons with missing
skulls might indicate that the animal had been trapped
by a collector and the skull removed for specimen
purposes. A pile of skeletons, or a number in a small
area, may consist of such animals as coyotes or bobcats and, if so, it suggests that they had been taken
and skinned by the trapper. Predatory animal trappers become most skillful at their work, and their
monthly catch is astonishingly large if they are in a
territory that has not been exhaustively trapped for
some time. Doc mentioned that on the Clover Flat
road he had found a place where a predatory animal
trapper had brought together and skinned thirty or
forty bobcats. This had taken place in the previous
winter, and the skeletons were not yet entirely clean.
As skulls were always needed in the classroom for
specimens and class work, he had brought in about
half of them to clean up later. On the plateau above
Murphy Hot Springs, he located a pile of beaver
skeletons which were so old that they crumbled between his fingers. Doc said that some imaginative reporter would have ascribed them to the early trappers
and would have justified the location by saying that
the trappers, constantly exposed to Indian raids, had

put their camp on the high spot so they could have a commanding view and thus protect themselves against surprise attacks.

We found skeletons everywhere. Once we found a coyote with a billeted trap attached to its leg. The trap had been dragged far enough so that the trapper had not been able to find it. It would have been more merciful if the trapper had located it, for the poor beast had met a slow and miserable death. At another time we found the remains of four beef cattle at the foot of a cliff and in a small rock alcove. We wondered if the owner had ever discovered them.

Often we found skeletons near dry washes. The animals had mired in wet and loose sand and had not been strong enough to extricate themselves. In one case the skeletons were in soil as hard and well baked as adobe bricks. Doc said that at one camp he noticed the skeleton of a cow, almost hidden by bushes along the creek where he had been getting his drinking water for the past few days. It proved, he said, that one never can be exactly sure what kind of territory his drinking water has passed through.

The talk about the quality of the drinking water reminded Wyomin' of a man's body in the river near the camp where he had been working one summer. When the camp was discussing the matter after dinner, the exact location where the body was found was brought up. One man said it was floating near the ferry; the man who drove the tank truck said it was fifty yards up from where the creek entered the river. As the argument got hot, the water tender said indignantly, "Well, I guess I ought to know. The coroner drove his car up the road where I take the tank wagon; the body was just beyond a floating log and

not more than two rods above where I get water every day."

Occasionally we see the skeleton of a sheep. Some of these have been old or lame ones which could not keep up with the band, and so they are killed and the pelts taken and the carcasses used for food, or, if in bad condition, left behind. Sickness takes some; predators account for a few, but that loss has been decreasing annually because the number of coyotes has been cut down.

Most of the skeletons were those of mammals. Those of birds were seldom seen. Desert animals vary in size from tiny mice to cattle and horses. Like the bones of smaller mammals, those of birds are so delicate that they are quickly destroyed. Nevertheless, the dry conditions of the desert are probably more favorable to the preservation of skeletons than are those of any other area we had visited.

Proper identification was not difficult for Doc and Wyomin'. I soon learned that the skulls were considered the most important part of a skeleton and the most valuable for identification. Since they are extremely hard bone, particularly the teeth, they preserve well. Often the only remaining part of a skeleton and even of the skull will be the jawbones bearing the teeth. Either of the two men could pick up such a fragment and say, "That's from a badger," or a pocket gopher, or whatever the case might be. The skulls of all orders, families, and genera of mammals are quite distinctive, and the species can be recognized as well, with a little closer attention to details; even some of the subspecies can be determined.

Scientists have developed the science of craniology (skull study) to a high degree. The skull is excellent for identification purposes because it has so many parts which vary, in combination or separately. This gives an almost infinite variety of combinations of parts: in their shape, size, and location; and in types of teeth, their arrangement, and the pattern of prominences on cutting surfaces, all of which are characteristic of the kind of mammal to which they belong.

This is no place for scientific discussion, but a few examples will show the apparently small characteristics which are used to separate mammals. For example:

The final decision as to whether an animal is a squirrel is determined not by bushy tails and perky manners but by the spinelike processes, or growths, on the frontal bone just behind the location of the eyeball.

We all think we know cats, but the scientist wants first to know that the specimen in question has the following characteristics—a skull relatively short and rounded, and the last tooth in the upper jaw row very small in relation to the other jaw teeth and turned inward. This characteristic separates cats from the other carnivores.

Can you tell the domestic dog from its wild brother, the coyote? You may base your judgment on external appearance, but the real test seems to be this complicated formula: in the coyote the length of the upper molar tooth row divided by the palatal width (width of plate) is 3.1 or more, while in domestic dogs it is usually less than 2.7.

Even a little creature like the harvest mouse must be judged by its teeth. If you want to separate this mouse from the other mice in Owyhee you must be sure that its upper incisors are not smooth but have a longitudinal groove on the anterior face.

Just one more example. All rodents and rabbits can be told from other mammals by certain teeth patterns. Neither have any canines (fangs or eye teeth) but a space called a diastema between the incisors and pre-molars. And if you want to tell the rabbits and rodents apart, you can do so positively if you know that the rodents have just one pair of incisors in the upper jaw, while the rabbits have four incisors, one pair of small incisors *behind* (unusual in mammals) the front pair.

If you are inclined to say "So what?" to this rather lengthy discussion, let me explain why it is really of great importance. It seems easy to describe in a few words the difference between, let us say, rabbits and rodents. But if you saw all kinds of each, you would find that the rabbits vary so much that some of them approach the external characteristics and appearance of the rodents; and the rodents vary so much that some look to us like rabbits. So the scientists have been forced to find characteristics which all of the rabbits have and none of the rodents have, and to look for others possessed only by rodents. Then experts the world over can agree which is which.

Bone relics of the recent past are not the only ones to be found in the Owyhee area. The county is rich in fossils and includes conifers and deciduous trees, fish, and many large mammals such as mastodons, horses, mammoths, camels, bison, and many other animals. Most of them have been dug up in the lake-bed country. Professor Edward F. Rhodenbaugh, of Boise, Idaho, has described them thoroughly, and anybody interested can find much detailed information in his book *Sketches of Idaho Geology,* and other material.

Our great interest is in other fields of endeavor and our contact with fossils has been more or less accidental, although one cannot traverse the desert lake country without coming in contact with evidences of these early periods. On one occasion we visited the shore of a onetime lake off the Riddle road from Bruneau. Fossils were strewn about like material left by the tides on the Pacific. Included were pieces of different woods, parts of fish, mollusks, and animals, badly broken up but distinct in origin. I have never seen anything as natural as the wood pieces. One might have thought them chips, twigs, slivers, and knots brought up on a beach where they had been bleached by the sun and polished by the drifting sands. I brought a box of them to my home in Seattle where I mixed them with small pieces of driftwood picked up on a Washington beach. I made them into a form similar to that of a tepee campfire and, so similar were the fossils and the wood, they could not be told apart without handling.

As I had read something of the geological history of western Idaho, I did not think the presence of fossils in large quantities was strange. There had been periods when the land was elevated, and these had alternated with those when the land was depressed and covered with lakes of many thousands of square miles. The climate had been moist and the exposed land was covered in places by great savannahs. Erosion, volcanism, stands of timber, all had a part in the history of the area. It is a history of slow but steady change. The present lack of concealing vegetation in much of Owyhee County makes the record easy to read, as compared with the timbered districts of the Pacific slope.

At the camp one night when we were discussing skeletons past and present, Wyomin' remarked, "There's one kind of remains we haven't mentioned."

"What kind do you mean?"

"Automobile remains. I don't know where they come from, but they're scattered around the desert like animal remains. Everythin' any good is gone. They're just like the shells of what used to be 'Gallopin' Gerties.' They get me to wonderin' just as I do when I see animal bones."

"Now you mention it, we do see a lot of them," I said. "But what do you wonder about?"

"Where do they come from? How do they get there? Each car raises a question. There's a story behind every one of them."

"I suppose there is," said Doc.

"The cars all look different," said Wyomin'. "Did the owners strip the parts off and leave the cars because they thought they were sufferin' from too expensive a disease (repair bills) to cure? I saw one with three bullet holes in the back. Did some hunter who wanted to practice use it for a target? Or was there some kind of a chase which ended in the shootin' and the capture of the occupants? I saw one at the bottom of a cliff as steep as where we saw the four cattle. Did it run off accidentally or did the owner just head it down, then get out and let it take a crash dive? Some of the cars are thirty years old. Others are maybe fifteen. I'd like to know something about them."

"So would I," said Doc. "But, after all, we'll be the rest of our lives just trying to find out about animals. I guess we had better leave the auto wrecks for those fellows who make a business of hunting up strange happenings for radio and TV shows."

"Suits me," replied Wyomin'. "But if you ever hear of any such programs, I wish you'd let me know."

CHAPTER XXI

Pronghorn

The sky was dark and threatening as we drove along the road from the Mud Flat country toward Big Spring. Wyomin' had been napping as we had ascended the long grade from Grandview, but the tremendous crashes of thunder that had echoed among the high peaks along Poison Creek had awakened him. Now he sat alertly upright, his keen eyes scanning the rolling country ahead of the car.

I wondered what this trip would bring. The weather certainly had changed from the low country. Down there in the desert the sky was clear and the air hot. Just a few puffy thunderheads projected above the rim of the Owyhee escarpment. Here, up on the high plateau to which we had come, one of Doc's "cold lows" was in charge. Thunder muttered ominously around the horizon, while blobs of fog swept over the scattered patches of mountain mahogany and juniper. The road seemed somewhat better than average but it was very crooked and Doc drove the station wagon slowly and carefully.

Around one of the twists in the road we came to a little flat with a small corral in its center. On the far side of the corral rose two rocky outcroppings terminating in points about fifty feet high. Between these two projections lay a sort of natural gateway that revealed a grassy swale several hundred yards farther to the west. The corral was simply but adequately built of materials available from the immediate vicinity. The upright posts had been cut from juniper trees and were placed in the ground a few feet apart. Interlaced horizontally between the posts was a thick fencing of mountain mahogany branches to form a crude but effective barrier.

Doc slowed the car down slightly as we came up by the corral. Suddenly Wyomin' spoke.

"Rein her in, Doc, I think I see a big fat ground hog right on top of that south point beyond the corral. I bet I can get him for you. Eohippus, what a wad of excelsior he'll take for stuffin'!"

Doc pulled the car over by the side of the road and the three of us piled out. Wyomin' took out his .22 rifle and laid it over the hood of the car. Crouching behind it, he squinted professionally down the sights. As the distance was rather long, Doc chuckled.

"Are you actually planning to hit it?" he asked.

"Sure thing," said Wyomin'. "Right in the neck, in fact."

Not particularly interested in observing the demise of the chuck, I swept the area to the west with my binoculars. Upon peering through the notch between the outcroppings, I saw a group of five antelope in the middle of the grassy swale.

"Hold 'er up, Wyomin'," I called. "I've got some antelope on that flat beyond the points. Let's take a look at them."

Wyomin' put down his gun while Doc got out his camera and telephoto lenses. While Wyomin' and I sat down on a couple of flat rocks, Doc began setting up the heavy tripod for the camera.

"You know, boys," began Wyomin', "every time I see some antelope I think about the bad winter the folks and I had back in Wyomin'. If ever there was a winter that you could speak of as 'the big snow,' that was it. In some places the snow drifted so deep you couldn't tell the drifts from the regular mountains. The road, all forty miles of it, was completely blocked. No way of getting to town, even if we had the money to buy anything, which we didn't. So we were stuck on the ranch with beans, bacon, flour, and coffee, and were getting downright tired of that bill of fare when Dad happened to go over by Warm Spring Flat one day. There he found that a good-sized herd of antelope were holed up. Gosh, we practically lived on antelope till the thaw came. Then we got busy and buried all the bones and such so some nosy game warden wouldn't get curious in the summer. But I think he would have done the same thing if he had been in our fix."

Wyomin' stopped talking to watch a particularly fat ground squirrel, one of several playing around the corral.

"Corrals are certainly good places for squirrels," he said. "Have you noticed, Doc, how many squirrels we've collected near corrals and old homesteads? Must be something that attracts them around places where humans and animals have been. You might work on that, sometime, Doc."

"That's Project Number 999 on this expedition," replied Doc, somewhat wearily.

Thunder rolled and muttered to the south. That storm's getting closer, I thought. I noticed that there were fewer ground squirrels in sight. The antelope still moved slowly around the grassy swale, apparently unconcerned by the darkening and lowering sky.

"Now, when you come to speed," continued Wyomin', "the antelope really has it. He's built for fast travelin' and he certainly likes to run, just for the fun of it. He runs smoothly, with very little rise at each jump. I remember reading somewheres that leaps of at least twenty-seven feet have been recorded for antelope. The same fellow thought that twelve to fourteen feet would be average for a jump. Put bounces like that together pretty fast and you have some real speed. Dad says that he has paced antelope at between thirty-five and forty miles an hour with his car in Wyomin'. Dad also thinks that bucks and does hold their heads differently when running. The bucks run with their horns pointing forward and the muzzle pointing downward, while the does point their noses straight out in front."

The thunder in the south rolled ever more loudly and ominously. I noticed that there were now no more ground squirrels to be seen around the corral flat.

"I suppose that you have hunted quite a few antelope, then, from what you say," asked Doc of Wyomin'.

"You bet," replied the latter. "There's a real test of skill, to start out after one of those fast-bouncing fellows. It would take quite a shot to hit a light brown streak flashing along the desert. However, they have a curious aspect to them and, with a little skill at deception and actin' mysterious-like, I can usually manage to sneak up fairly close to them. And, of course, my .270 rifle really reaches out to them."

"How smart do you think they are?" asked Doc.

"Oh, just average, I would say," answered Wyomin'. "They got pretty sharp eyesight, though, as most open-country critters have, and they can usually see you before you see them, if you both are in the open. My old evolution teacher in college would probably say that good eyesight and fast legs were adaptations for living in an open, exposed habitat where there was very little cover. The antelope's leg has no dew-claws, you know, and is really streamlined for running. Just about the best foot for running, short of the horse's single toe."

"It must be a terrible thing," I mentioned, "to be in constant fear of losing one's life and having to be continually on the alert for any predatory enemy. Yet they seem to have survived pretty well—that is, till man and the rifle came along. These wildlife management people like to talk about a thousand and one factors in a game animal's existence, but I have always thought that if you leave Nature alone, it will pretty well take care of itself in establishing the balance possible in any particular place. I once heard a well-known biologist and wildlife expert speak about the factors affecting animals and then end his talk by mentioning the possible existence of certain 'cosmic influences' that might be important, too. I wondered at the time if he could be alluding to two-legged hunters with .30-30 carbines."

The cumulus cells had moved up from the south

by this time and, although the sky was evenly black-
ish, hot spots of lightning activity warned us that there
were several thunderheads bearing down on us. A
rapidly increasing splatter of raindrops indicated, as
the medics put it, a prescription of shelter, so we retreated to the station wagon. In a few minutes the
rain gush hit us in earnest. The hard-baked ground
around the corral was covered with bouncing splashes
of water. Down on the swale, we could barely see
the antelope huddled together.

After looking at them through the binoculars, Wyomin' shook his head and said, "When I was little, I
thought I would like to be an antelope, if I had to
change from being a human. But now, I'm not so
sure. You know, Frank, those poor beasts are out in
every kind of weather that comes along."

"What would you rather be, then, Wyomin'? One
of those ground squirrels over by the corral?" I asked,
while Doc laughed.

"Well," replied Wyomin', "at least they're down
where it's nice and dry right now, but that long
winter sleep doesn't appeal too much to me. I like
to be out and around and seein' what's goin' on.
Six months out of action is too long for me."

"This seems to have developed into quite an antelope session," I said. "And to think that people say
that women do all the talking. What have you to
offer, Doc?"

"I've just been thinking about the name of the
animal," said Doc. "Names are funny things, just like
the white-bellied variety—*albiventris*—of the yellow-
bellied chipmunk, *Eutamias amoenus luteiventris*.
Our Rocky Mountain goat isn't a goat at all, but be-
longs to a group called the goat-antelopes, a European

representative of which would be the chamois. Now, we have been speaking of the animals down in that swale as 'antelope.' Actually they aren't in the true antelope group, but represent a single living species of the mammalian family Antilocapridae. This family is distinguished, among other things, by having true hollow horns, as in the cattle and sheep, but the horns are shed each year, the only species among the hollow-horned group where this takes place. Since the horns have a prong, this species, known technically as *Antilocapra americana*, has been called the prong-horn, which is really a better name than antelope. There are several subspecies of pronghorn ranging from southern Canada to northern Mexico and from the western Great Plains to the western margin of the Great Basin. It is, however, considerably scarcer now than it was a hundred years ago.

"One usually finds pronghorns in open country—plains or barren, rolling hills. It seems to be one hoofed animal that does very well in very poor land. Poor, that is, from the standpoint of what would make good deer or elk country. Desert habitat often is very favorable for them. They like such things as antelope brush—often called bitter brush in Idaho—and sagebrush, and seem able to get enough water from their feed when water holes are lacking in the dry season. However, they are not adverse to getting into ranchers' hay meadows."

The rain had stopped and the storm had passed to the north. Broken sky toward the Nevada line revealed a few patches of bright blue. In a few minutes the sun broke through the remaining clouds, so we again resumed our outdoor seats and broke out our lunches. A couple of antelope were still in sight and

we saw a solitary ground squirrel appear near the far corral fence. Considerably farther to the west the Juniper Mountains loomed as a dark, wooded ridge. I hoped that we could get into that area sometime for, as far as we know, no naturalist has ever visited them. I mentioned my thoughts to Doc and Wyomin' and they echoed my desire to see this unknown area. Unfortunately, as Wyomin' put it, just about the best way to get to them was to start walking.

Doc resumed his description of the habits of the pronghorn:

"Along in the spring, the doe moves to areas that have good cover in fairly high country where she can have a good view of the surrounding desert to guard against enemies. It is here that the young are born, a single fawn, often twins in good habitat, or rarely triplets. In Idaho, the fawns are usually dropped in May. Enemies of the little fellows are sometimes common and they must lie very still oftentimes to avoid detection by the coyotes, bobcats, and eagles.

"As a student of animal coloration, the color pattern of the pronghorn has intrigued me. The brownish-tan of the upper parts, with the few darker facial markings, contrasts pleasingly with the lighter sides, rump, and neck bars. That rump patch is really something. I remember reading in one of Ernest Thompson Seton's books when I was just a few years old about the 'heliograph' that these animals carry. The white hairs on the rump are long, reaching a length of more than three inches. By means of dermal muscles, the pronghorn can erect these hairs to form a large white disk. In the bright desert sunshine, the sudden enlargement of the white area on the rump gives the illusion of a flash of white light. This behavior apparently serves the purpose of a warning system and can be seen at a considerable distance. The hair of the pronghorn is coarse and pithy and gives the animals good protection from desert heat and cold.

"If you examine the horns, you will see that they appear to be fibrous or hairlike in structure. This is true of all the horned animals because the horn material itself, unlike the antlers of the deer family, is a skin derivative— as is hair. Unlike the deer which shed their antlers, the horned mammals keep their horns as permanent appendages. The pronghorns, however, shed their horns annually. Actually, the horns represent an outer covering over a bony core which is a part of the skull itself. In the fall, the horny sheath is shed and the new horn begins to grow at the tip of the core. From the tip, the horny tissue grows down over the core till it meets the head. The tissue on the upper part of the horn enlarges to form the point and prong. By late winter, the horns of the bucks have reached their full growth and have become quite hard. Horns are formed in both sexes in the same fashion and are often rather similar in appearance, so that one has to depend on the black neck patch of the male for certain identification at a distance.

"Pronghorn tracks are quite similar to those of the deer, but in the pronghorn the hind border is usually broader and somewhat less curved than in the deer. An expert sometimes has trouble in separating pronghorn and mule deer on the basis of their tracks."

"What's the commonest sound that you have heard them make?" I asked Wyomin', as Doc paused to take another telephoto picture of the two antelope.

"Well," replied Wyomin', "I would say something close to the loud whistle that the white-tailed deer gives, but with a little more musical quality. The fawns have a soft bleat when answering their mother. I have observed antelope that I was sneakin' up on, and that had gotten my wind, stamp their hoofs like they were troubled and wanted to know what was going on."

"Although the mule deer and elk occasionally are found in fairly open situations," joined in Doc, "I have always considered the pronghorn to be the most typical of the plains and desert hoofed mammals. It is an animal that is usually found nowhere else and, if you want to use an ecologic indicator, that species is a good one. Incidently, I remember a paper written on antelope remains in eastern Washington by Dr. Douglas Osborne, Curator of Anthropology of the Washington State Museum, and published in a 1953 issue of *The Scientific Monthly*, entitled 'Archaeological Occurrences of Pronghorn Antelope, Bison, and Horse in the Columbia Plateau.' A number of house pits and caves were excavated which were found to contain bones of these three animals at places in the Columbia Basin. Briefly, Dr. Osborne found that pronghorns had been present in the Basin during prehistoric times and possibly as late as the 1600's; then they had become practically extinct in Washington. A few remained until the coming of the first whites. Osborne could see no good reason why the antelope disappeared from such a favorable habitat in the Basin area, but he suggests that climatic changes may have altered the country sufficiently to make the region unfavorable for antelope in sufficient numbers to persist or that some epidemic disease may have been the eliminating factor. The 'little ice age' of Matthes that appeared some four thousand years ago and tapered off down almost to the present may be responsible, through colder winters and deeper snows. An influx of northern predators may have upset the balance that made eastern Washington habitable for antelope. The antelope have remained in eastern Oregon, a still drier and warmer area than eastern Washington, which has persisted as an antelope range to the present."

I mentioned that the Washington State Game Department had reintroduced antelope into barren areas north of Yakima on an experimental basis. Irrigation has practically eliminated most of the former antelope range in central Washington, however, and it is probably questionable whether the animal will ever again become much of a game species in that state.

The sky had temporarily cleared. Doc took his pictures, and we had finished our lunch and were preparing to push on when a neat, gray pickup truck came along the road and pulled over beside us. A slim, black-haired, pleasant-mannered young fellow got out and walked over to us. He introduced himself as one of the two Owyhee County game wardens. He knew about Doc's work, of course, and asked him how he was getting along. Doc mentioned that we had stopped to get some pictures of antelope and had just been talking about them at some length.

The warden seemed to have a special interest in antelope and had, in fact, been just out on a trip checking their numbers in part of the Owyhee Range. He said that the total population in Idaho was estimated at approximately fifteen thousand head. Most of the antelope occur along the headwaters of the

Big and Little Lost rivers, the Lemhi and Pahsimeroi drainages, along Birch and Crooked creeks, and from the line between Arco and Mud Lake in Butte and Jefferson counties north to Salmon. Doc mentioned that he had studied a large group of the animals in the Lost River Range on Methodist Creek several years ago. In fact, every time he had set up a camp in that region, he was visited by a few curious individuals the first day, to see what he was up to.

By means of live trapping and transplanting, state biologists have established small herds in the Snake River Plains area north and south of Lake Walcott and in such places in Owyhee as the Jack's Creek area and around Big Spring, with scattered groups elsewhere, the warden continued. Doc mentioned that he had seen several antelope at about 8,100 feet on Quicksilver Mountain and some over on Boone Peak to the south. A certain number of antelope were said to work back and forth between Oregon and Idaho on the west side of the county.

The warden mentioned that the antelope did not seem to be doing quite as well in Owyhee as some people thought they should, and that the state was considering sending in a biologist to investigate the general antelope situation. I mentioned the observation that the interior herds might have a wintering problem. The fact that the animals had not been very common before introduction in the county might indicate some submarginal qualities to the region, as far as pronghorn habitat is concerned.

We were talking about this study project when an old, battered truck with a couple of unshaven young fellows drove up to us, slowed down and looked us over, and then continued on and disappeared. The warden watched the truck pass out of sight and slowly shook his head.

Wyomin' spoke up.

"You know, one of the things affecting antelope numbers might be poaching. Do you find much of it around Owyhee?"

"Poaching is certainly a factor, all right," answered the warden. "Just last week I found where five deer had been killed and cleaned about three miles north of Silver City. Actually, there are several kinds of poachers. The worst kind, in my estimation, is the city fellow—like some guy from Boise—who drives up here, knocks off a sage hen or two, covers them up and takes them back to town. He really doesn't need the meat. He's just breaking the law in its simplest form. Some of the old-timers around here lived in Owyhee before game regulations and have never gotten used to seasons. One might say that they are just a little careless in minding the law. On the other hand, some of the prospectors and miners are trimmed so close to the wind financially that they need some game once in a while, if they are to eat any fresh meat at all. The same is true of the sheepherders. Several times I have watched herders take a carbine from camp and sneak around through the buckbrush after a deer. Certainly, if anybody is entitled to some 'informal' game, the prospectors and sheepherders are.

"Of course, there are a lot of people around here who wouldn't think of shooting an animal out of season, even if it were on their place eating them out of house and home. And there are also several kinds of game wardens. Some I know work at the sleuthing business day and night, and drag in everybody they can catch. Others seem to overlook some poachers.

Personally, I have thought that the only way to enforce the law is to penalize everybody who goes astray, regardless of the circumstances. Of course, in so doing, I have been shot at a couple of times."

"Do you really mean that some people take their 'hunting' that seriously around here?" asked Doc.

"Oh yes," replied the warden. "Some conservation officers think that half the game taken in the county is poached, but there is almost no way to determine such a figure when you come right down to it. Actually, I have no idea what the number of illegal kills might be. Keeping them down is where I come in, I guess."

"Well, frankly," said Doc, "I think I would rather trap mice than lawbreakers. Nobody minds my killing all the mice I can get my hands on."

The game warden laughed.

"It's just like Lower Slobbovia. 'Either you eats the wolf, or the wolf eats you.' Well, I've got to get along. Glad to have seen you fellows. Be sure to come around for dinner the next time you're in Oreana."

We waved to the warden as he started his pickup and drove on north. He was barely out of sight when the old truck that had passed to the south a few minutes before came back up the road and stopped beside Doc's station wagon. The two characters, with a month's growth of beard and dirty Levi's and Mackinaws climbed down and staggered over toward us. One had a partly consumed can of beer in his hand. I noticed a carbine half under the seat of the truck. They eyed us narrowly for a couple of seconds and then one asked Doc if that had been the game warden's truck stopped beside us. Doc said that it had.

One of the pair turned to the other.

"Shall we go git him?" he asked.

"Naw," said his partner. "We can pick him off some other time."

The pair nodded to us and turned and walked back to their truck. After some effort, they got it started and began to roll along. We sat silently as the ancient vehicle with its homicidal contents lurched down the rocky road and out of sight beyond the next rise.

"Doc," I said, "if you ever write that in a book, nobody will believe you."

"Aw," laughed Wyomin', "they stopped believin' him long ago. Incidentally, that ground hog's back up on the point again," he said, as he picked up the rifle and slipped off the safety catch. "Watch me git *him!*"

CHAPTER XXII

When Shadows Fall

We stopped the car at the end of the trail-like lane which was the only approach to the sand dunes of Bruneau. Doc ignored the sand loop, at one time used as a turn around; the sagebrush branches and pieces of old sacks indicated clearly that it was too soft for safety. So he backed, filled and hauled on the narrow road until he got the car headed in the homeward direction—a precaution which he never neglected in rough country. We pointed the car so the lights, when turned on, would focus on a sloping surface of sand. There we poured out a package of rolled oats. We would be able to watch any rats or mice that might come to feed on it.

When Doc walked over to read the recording instrument which he had placed in the sand, he found a small and daintily patterned snake coiled up on the larger of the boxes. As Doc approached, it immediately dived for an open kangaroo rat hole near by, but Doc was quick enough to grasp it by the tail and transfer it to the empty rolled oats container.

It was long and slender, with dark patches on the back broken by yellow and red bands. It proved to be a long-nosed snake, regularly a dweller in the Southwest, but only the second specimen ever reported in Idaho.

It was 7:00 P.M. Every place we looked, the desert was red, as red as the color in a Kodachrome film exposed just before sunset. The gray of the sage appeared faintly tinged, the brown sand almost rosy, the few shrubs looked like some kind of exotic ornamentals. The dunes themselves seemed made of warm velvet with a texture which reflected different shades of the color.

Wyomin' looked at the close of this desert day. "Doc," he said, "if you weren't willin' to come along with us, I believe I would have argued about this assignment. It's just contrary to my bringin' up. I get up early, as you know. I've often gone to bed directly after leavin' the supper table. But I never before reported for a job that began at 7:30 P.M. and lasted all night. It just doesn't go with a farm education."

"Maybe this will put a few ideas in your head," said Doc, "a few ideas about how to live. We'll walk over to the dunes and look around. Then we can come back a little later and get the equipment."

This all-night vigil on the desert was a new one for us, although we had had such sessions on Mount Pilchuck and elsewhere. Most of our desert experiences had been in full daylight, supplemented by short excursions at daybreak or dusk. Yet night is the period of greatest activity on the desert. Doc estimates that there are about one hundred species of Idaho mammals. Approximately eighty out of the one hundred are almost completely nocturnal. The tree squirrels (except the flying squirrels), the ground squirrels, and chipmunks are diurnal.

It is not difficult to understand why animals of the desert are largely nocturnal. The problem of the hunted is to get their sustenance without being picked up for the sustenance of others. The eaters of vegetation, to whose bodies most of the predators look for food, range freely after dark, probably because of the freedom from extreme heat and the greater protection afforded by night. The predators hunt when their prey is available and, to exist, they must take a reasonable number of unwary, maimed, or slow-moving victims. Night activity is therefore greatest. Would it be possible to investigate this period?

We decided to try it. We had been warned against moving around after dark because of the rattlesnakes. Probably they might be waiting for careless victims, but we would have to take that risk. We had planned carefully. We had chosen the Bruneau area because the dunes were the largest in the state and yet the most easily reached.

Now we are at the dunes. Three horned larks flew by, calling. We walk through the drifted sagebrush toward the great sand piles which lie ahead. A faint odor of burning sagebrush comes to us from a range fire some miles away. The breeze through the cheat grass and sagebrush makes the only sound until a shrike sings close by. A magpie flies low and squawks mockingly as it passes.

Meanwhile, the tops of the dunes remain reddish, but the lower parts are almost violet. Five Brewer's sparrows rise from the brush. The sand is covered with gray and yellow grasshoppers; they fly in all directions when we disturb them. A burrowing owl rises from a small bluff to the south and begins hunting over the sagebrush. At 7:45 P.M. the sun is just above the horizon. Several dragonflies, whose wings are marked black and white, fly at a speed which makes a leaping jack rabbit beneath them look as if it were walking.

As we come to one of the water holes, jacks which have been drinking leave in all directions. Our presence does not alarm them greatly; they move with their accustomed wariness, but without any sudden dashes which would show that they were alarmed. We chance to look up and see seven ravens whose flight had been noiseless enough to prevent us from hearing them. A Wilson's phalarope leaves noiselessly but speedily. Two killdeers reverse the procedure; they fly much more slowly and set up a continual shrilling which fills the whole area. In the sand ahead of me I see a small, oval-shaped beetle with silver bands separating the head, thorax, and abdominal regions. When I stoop to pick it up, five mallards, startled by my sudden motion, burst from the far side of the pond and start off with a prodigious whirring of wings.

The open surfaces of the water holes, riffled by the breeze, are a striking violet color; but in the sheltered margins, where the water is smooth, it has taken on a copper hue which reflects the hues of the sand.

Wyomin' breaks the silence. "It's just a mile from the road but it's a lonesome scene. Nothin' to remind you of civilization when you look toward the dunes. They make you think of far-off places."

At one minute after eight the sun drops behind the dunes, which lose their brown color and turn grayish. We discover signs of wild horses around the pond, with a few coyote tracks and a regular trail made by badgers. The dragonflies evidently find hunting good, for they hover over the pond. The temperature drops noticeably. No sound now, except the flutter of grasshoppers as we walk. Occasionally a jack starts from the brush and disappears over a near-by dune, making the ascent in powerful leaps and stopping for a moment at the crest.

We find a water hole surrounded by quicksand. We locate two more small holes in the same condition—the first quicksand we have seen in the area, although it is often a part of the desert scene. We see no animal tracks around these pools as animals avoid places where footing is insecure. The distant mountains are now a deep blue.

Two mourning doves fly away from a water hole larger than the others, and with cattails around its edges. The sand dunes are now pinkish gray. Two dragonflies spiral higher and higher, coupled in mating flight. They fly across the face of the moon—new life in process of creation. The sand is still warm to the touch. The cooling air has become slightly turbulent so that pockets of warm and cool air alternately strike our faces.

At eight twenty-six we come to the big water hole, or what's left of it. The large dunes stay in position pretty well, but there is plenty of change in the smaller ones. We find an acre-size water hole complete with cattails in what, two or three years ago, was a pass between two dunes. Such extreme topographical changes must affect the ecology as well. Rather a precarious existence for animals dependent on water holes. What saves them is the existence of water in some parts of the area. If the holes all disappeared, the animals would be in bad shape.

A herd of about a dozen range horses, including three white ones, come to the opposite side to drink. They are very nervous and watchful. The young colts seem very proud, carrying their heads erect. Perhaps the freedom of the range gives them this bearing of independence. A family of coots, the young, five in number and fairly well grown, utter their sharp alarm notes as they move to the unoccupied end of the pond. They swim into the water weeds, while a poorwill drops close to the water and a killdeer flies noisily away.

We watch the show, saying little and talking in low tones when we have anything to say, as one might talk while waiting for a funeral service to begin. Every sight, every sound, takes us farther away from civilization and puts us deeper into the feeling and mood of the desert. On the way back to the car to pick up the lights, we hear a barking in the dunes. It sounds like a fox, and Wyomin' expresses the hope that it might be a kit fox, that diminutive edition which we have continually sought but never found, although its skull has been collected in the county.

At the car we listen to the nine o'clock news report on the radio. Temporarily it breaks our mood, for plenty is happening out in civilization; but, when it is turned off, the desert crowds in again and our thoughts are of its sands and its denizens. We discuss the temperature changes, for the air temperature is now 70° Fahrenheit and the burrow has risen slightly, to 68°. We pose the question as to whether evening temperature or change in light makes a mouse come out. Light would not be useful as an indicator to a creature which plugs its burrow with a front door of sand. The breeze has temporarily stopped. There is still a faint glow in the west. The moon is exceedingly bright. We hear a faint hum of mosquitoes and the chirping of crickets around the car.

In spite of the moonlight, we have to turn on the car lights to watch the pile of rolled oats. Kangaroo rats are the most frequent visitors to the pile which is steadily diminishing. Deer mice have begun a sampling. It is Doc's opinion that there will be many happy meals on rolled oats this winter, for this is harvest time for rodents and much that is taken away will be added to the winter stores. When we turn on the lights again, we see a pocket mouse. Usually they don't come around if there are rats present. As soon as the light struck it, the timid creature scampered away.

What a precarious existence the mice have; just existing, as it were, for the purpose of reproducing their kind. Just marking time, you might say; but, from the long view, they are not marking time, because their kinds are slowly involved in the process of evolution. The goal of evolution has been said to be to fill all of the ecological niches with an animal specifically designed by natural selection to live in that niche. Evolution is a perfection of the adaptation of the niche occupants. The individual mouse is merely a link, of which there are many duplicates, in this chain. The only purpose of life is to continue life. This is true of all animals except humans. Humans have tried to make their lives less tedious and more enjoyable. Some people think that there must be more to the living world than this, as far as the lower animals are concerned. If so, science has revealed nothing of this hypothesis.

We check the instruments again. One of the thermographs in the open measures temperature in the air one inch above the ground. The other is placed to read at twelve inches above ground. The lower one is now six degrees cooler than the upper one. The air near the ground will cool more, because of radiation of heat from the sand. On the previous Saturday, with a weather cold front, the surface layer cooled to 38° but rose to 108° the following day—seventy degrees difference.

The almost full moon has now brilliantly lighted the light-colored sand and the almost-bleached vegetation. A large owl flies by, just a dark blur against the stars. It is the winged hunter of the night feeding on the little rats and mice. It is amazing how it can see its prey in the very weak light of the stars. It hovers noiselessly over the mouse a foot or two above the rodent, then suddenly drops down on the ground, sweeping it with its large wings and clutching the unlucky animal with its sharp talons.

The quietness is most impressive. The noises we do hear are strange ones. I can see how the tenderfoot feels all alone at night when the sense of sight becomes almost useless and the sense of hearing becomes the dominant one. There are no familiar and reassuring sounds. The noises he hears puzzle and disturb him.

We notice the increasing coolness. A few more rats have begun to prowl around. A light breeze is now blowing from the east. Four hours ago we were perspiring. Now we are getting chilly enough to make a little exercise desirable. Occasionally we hear the hum of an airplane over near the Mountain Home Air Base; possibly some night maneuvers. Our feeling toward it is one of remoteness. Tonight we are not of the cities but of the desert.

From eleven thirty at night to one o'clock in the morning our windbreakers feel welcome, although the breeze is a little warmer. The desert is now almost white, a ghostly white. Meteorites flash frequently. No wonder the less educated peoples believed and still believe in ghosts. Anything might come down from those sharp dune crests. Wyomin' called it "grave-yardy." This desert would make a good place for the Scots' "bodach glas"—the double image of oneself supposed to presage death. It is a tale of the moors and the heather of the Highlands, but its setting could have been no stranger than these silver-bathed sands of Bruneau.

Between 1:00 A.M. and 2:00 A.M., we eat a few cookies and drink cool water from the thermos jugs. It is quiet now, except for the stars, the glow of the Mountain Home Air Base lights, and a faint, barely detectable change in the northeast. The moon has almost set and it is much darker. We hear the sound of coyotes in the distance. The sagebrush on the sand dunes is dark. A brilliant red star comes up in the east, very close to a bright white one. The Milky Way drips with brilliance.

We leave the car to make another round of the dunes. We cross the low ridge that marks the boundary between the sage-covered sand and the bare dunes and walk over to the closest water hole. The water shows up black in the dull light.

"Could you figure a better settin' for a mystery story?" asked Wyomin'. "The victim pursued by the mysterious phantom and gettin' lost in the trackless waste, gradually becomin' more and more frightened, until at last he stumbles into quicksand and slowly but painfully perishes? That would give the sleuth somethin' to worry about."

"We'd better not get too close to that shaky stuff or we might have something to worry about ourselves," I said.

Since the moon went down, the kangaroo rats have become active. Apparently there was too much light before for complete safety of operation. When we look over the trap line, half the traps have been sprung and the bait removed. Two rats taken made fine specimens for the museum collection. We spot several others in the glare of the flashlight as they hop around. They seem fairly shy, but can be approached within a few feet. They appear chalk white in the light—little fellows with large heads and long tails they drag behind them when walking; big, shiny eyes that reflect the light and glow; long hind legs that propel them with a series of hops without any dependence on the very short front ones.

At 3:25 A.M. the air temperature is 51° and, in the burrow, 71°. We succeed easily in locating the rats with the spotlight beam. Coyotes sound off in the southwest with one great crescendo which lasts for nearly four minutes. In most areas the animals have been greatly reduced by traps, poisoning, and cyanide gunnery, but it will be a long time before these canny and resourceful animals will be driven out of existence by man. In a few places they have actually increased in numbers in spite of the most constant and heavy persecution.

Owyhee appears to be one of the places where the

increase in coyote population has taken place. A friend of Doc's doing some field work in the desert said that while returning to camp after dark he noticed several animals close to him. At first he thought them sheep dogs from some near camp, but as he proceeded they circled him slowly and he saw they were coyotes. This kept up for perhaps half a mile, when suddenly the thought occurred that they might be following him. He didn't like it; for while he knew that one coyote was timid, there might be a different reaction if a half-dozen were bunched. They followed him all the way to camp, getting a little closer but making no move toward him. He admitted to being very uneasy because he knew that some of them had been reported as rabid and, as he said, he wouldn't care to have even a band of tame dogs prowling about him in the darkness. He got to the camp without accident and, when he fired his gun, the animals disappeared. He stated that since then he had found another man who had had a similar experience.

By 4:00 A.M. there appears a definite, though colorless, glow in the northeast. Slowly but steadily the blackness in front of us begins to dissolve, and we see the faint outlines of dunes and clumps of sage, as photographic images appear on the film in a developing tray. The activity of the rats around the car has definitely tapered off. Light dampens all activity except the one group of coyote serenaders.

By 5:00 A.M. it is light enough to read. We hear a ring-necked pheasant crowing in a distant field. Color glows in the east. A rooster joins the crowing pheasant. Sound certainly carries well here, and in few places have we ever been where the competition is so completely absent. A short-eared owl flies over.

Now the sky is bright orange in the east. The sound of farm trucks moving on the highway comes to us. The breeze picks up and foliage sways lightly. Temperature reading again—air 64°, surface 48°, burrow 72°. Rats will enter nice warm burrows when they leave the chilly sand.

Mourning doves are cooing, rabbits actively moving about. We hear the sound of the morning passenger train in the distance. Almost complete daylight. A horned lark flies by, calling.

Our conversational voices appear to strengthen with the coming of morning. All reason for the whispering which seemed so essential during the night has disappeared.

Wyomin' voiced his opinion of the night's experience. "I've learned one thing. I used to worry a bit about the hard time these small desert animals had in the terrific heat and unfavorable conditions. I believe I know better now. They stay in their burrows in the daytime when the temperature, according to our thermographs, is above one hundred degrees outside and enjoy a nice sixty degrees. At night when their burrows heat up some, they travel around in the high forties on the ground surface. It almost looks as if the desert habitat is among the best of all for small mammals. Maybe that's why there's so blamed many of them."

The air was quiet as we closed the car doors and moved away. Everywhere the soft sand recorded the activity of the night, including the route of our wanderings. It was all there, from the bulletlike marks of the short-coupled grasshoppers to the shadowed remains of our foot tracks. But soon, as the heated currents of air began to rise, the wind would come up and, like a great eraser, wipe out all marks, leaving the desert ready for the record of another night of activity.

CHAPTER XXIII

Desert Adaptations

We have spoken of a mile-high mountain in the Cascade Range of Washington where Doc and I spent much of our spare time for several years. Dark lines of cliffs or tumbled masses of rock stand above the timber line, except where snow and ice whiten the summit and reach down into the canyons. But below that area the trees grow so closely that only the greens of their foliage can be seen. It is not a uniform green, for the tree species vary at different altitudes and under different conditions. The floor beneath this lovely and impressive covering is in a shade which is always dark and, when the sky is heavily overcast, it resembles late twilight. The swift streams reflect this color. The undergrowth is shade-loving, with many lichens and mosses. The animals which live in the woods are dark colored and of inconspicuous pattern and, when they move about, they merge with the background in which they live.

Each country has its distinctive pattern. On the

Owyhee Desert, old lake beds are nearly white; most of the other features have light coloration. The sagebrush is gray and the other shrubs lack the dense greens of moister situations so that they are a gray-green. The Washington mountains resemble the quiet cloisters of a church or library; the Owyhee Desert has all the brightness and overpowering light of the seashore at midday. There are a few black birds such as the Brewer's blackbirds and the ravens, but most of the others are light-colored, including various shades of gray and tan. Like the dwellers in the mountains, they have assumed shades which will serve to protect them. As a result, they and other animals of the desert are, with few exceptions, attired in one or more of a series of what might be called "desert grays."

A Brewer's sparrow flew into a sagebush after our dinner one evening, while we were enjoying the sunset in camp. I looked closely to see where it had landed, but its long-tailed and small, slender body was not to be seen. The gray and brown of its coloration had blended with the sage so that I couldn't locate it. I mentioned the fact to Doc and Wyomin'.

"There's a Brewer's sparrow in that second sagebush, but I can't find it—they certainly match up with their backgrounds."

We all looked for the bird but did not see it until it flew from the bush and toward another clump a few yards away. Then something entirely unexpected occurred; we heard a swish overhead, followed by an alarmed cry from the sparrow. We saw a dark-colored pigeon hawk fly up, after an ineffective stoop or attack. It tried again and missed. By this time the sparrow was flying up, instead of seeking the shelter of a bush.

It sought to escape by flying cross-country, but was dive-bombed with near misses. The sparrow tried to get higher in the air and outfly the hawk but did not have the speed to evade it. The predator would fly still higher and make a folded-wing dive which was much faster than the sparrow's flight. The hawk's only method of attack seemed to be this direct and powerful plunge. The sparrow's tactic of trying to gain altitude was met by the circling of the hawk until it was higher up and ready for another attempt. We watched, our sympathy with the game fight of the small bird, but admiring the magnificent flight attack of the predator. We knew the result was certain. Two more dives of the hawk missed fire; then, on the third, the predator hit the sparrow and it plunged steeply with closed wings toward the earth. The sparrow struck the ground only a few feet ahead of the hawk. The hawk executed a rapid flip-over, wheeled, and perched by the dead bird preparatory to feeding.

It was a tragedy which we had seen many times before and which we would see repeated many times in the future. It appears cruel, but some birds must end as prey if predators are to live.

Doc broke the silence. "That's one place where coloration did not protect. In the bushes, the bird would have been safe. But in the open, with a hawk near by, its chance was gone. From the standpoint of the preyed-upon, adaptation's great value is to keep a creature out of trouble. After it runs into it, not much can be done."

"But color adaptation operates real well in the desert," said Wyomin'. "I've noticed that nearly all the local birds seem to have it. Nobody would doubt but that the gray flycatcher is a typical desert bird;

its color couldn't fit in better. All the sparrows are small and gray, or brown and inconspicuous. The burrowin' owl might be a lump when it sits near the entrance to its nest."

It is a fact. There are other examples even more striking. Sage hens, as big as small turkeys, are hard to spot when they stand quiet. Their black bellies and their bodies of gray and brown and black do not appear particularly suitable, but they do merge with the desert in a most effective way. I have been close to six or seven without noticing them until they got up and flew away. Horned larks, Swainson's hawks, and sage thrashers are marked differently, but all patterns seem to be adequate.

"Desert patterns do a pretty good job," said Doc. "It's so efficient, Wyomin', that you gave Frank some fine advice the other day when you told him to look for motion and not for the rabbit. That's the system you have to follow when you look for live things on the desert. You can't pick out a sitting bird in the brush. You have to look for movement of a branch, or a difference in shadow, or a change of position. That tells you something alive is there. Then, when you know it is there, you can begin to separate it from its surroundings. If you're lucky, you can spot it and find out what it is. I suppose it's particularly true in the Arctic where there's so much white and no contrast."

It is true in other places. I remembered the time when I was in high country with a friend who was hunting. We sat down for a moment and, as we looked over the hillsides, he remarked that there were deer on the second slope. When I asked how he could be sure at that distance, he replied simply, "Bushes and young pines stand still; the only big things which would be moving in that place are deer."

Because protective cover is usually scarce on the desert, protective coloration is one of the most important factors in successfully meeting desert conditions. Open terrain exposes animal life to predator attacks. Inconspicuousness is a protection, and it is carried to extreme lengths. Chipmunks, for example, which are found in many habitats, from the light sands of the deserts to the black rocks of the lava districts, will be found to have pelages which vary from the extremely light to the extremely dark, each species being adapted to the area which houses it. Everywhere on the desert we find this color response—an approximation in general color or pattern of the animal to the general color or pattern of its surroundings. A difference in habitat or in the use of that habitat means a difference in color. For example, the flycatchers which habitually occupy the greenish-gray bushes will have a different pattern from a sparrow which feeds and nests on the dun-colored sand.

Camouflage is not confined to the birds and the mammals. Perhaps the best illustration of this device is shown by the horned toads of Owyhee. These small lizards usually occupy gravelly ground where the sand has partially blown off and left spots of gravel and coarse sand, or where the coarse sand is scattered with vegetation—usually Indian hemp. The animals merge with the color of the sand and the gray rocks. They remain motionless unless closely approached and so are very hard to see. Gordon, the young student who accompanied us on our ice-hunting trip to the dunes, had the sharpest eye for them of anybody I have met. If the animals do move, it is only for a short dis-

tance, usually just to the shelter of a near-by rock
or bush. There they rest. The shadow of their bodies
on the sand might be most revealing, but it is avoided by their pressing the body flat so that its extended
edge meets the soil. This action effectually eliminates
any shadow and makes the animal appear like a tiny
bump or ridge on the sand. The other lizards of
Owyhee are active and some are quite speedy. But
here is a reptile, sluggish, unaggressive, and plentiful, which is able to exist with apparently but one
method of defense, camouflage. Some of the other
species of horned toads have a custom which may be
for defense but which has not been seen in the Owyhee
species of the desert horned toad—that is the remarkable habit of squirting blood from its eyes.

Among the amphibians, certain frogs are most adept
in changing color to match their surroundings. The
best example in Owyhee is the Pacific tree frog. We
have found this creature in many moist habitats. Its
body color always approximates that of the background
where it is found. In an area of dark water and
dark rocks, it may be a dark, greenish-brown. In
the open meadows where the grass and herbs are
green, the frog is very light green. For this reason
it remains effectively concealed. The grass or leopard
frog common in the moist meadows along the Snake
in northern Owyhee County has a background color
of green on the body which varies to match the shade
of grass, herbs, algae, etc., in which it is found.

That the study of coloration is somewhat involved
can be illustrated by a section which I excerpted
from Doc's notebook. It is a scientific note, but I
think the meaning is clear.

The kangaroo rats seem of a slightly different color in this area. That is, they seem somewhat lighter in the N.E. corner of the county. The deer mice appear noticeably lighter. This may be due to the presence of lake sediments and yellow sand. Specimens should be taken of the sand of the two areas (NE corner and Oreana) and photometer tests and correlations made in the laboratory. The various soils of the county should be examined, charted, and specimens taken of each. Next year, an attempt should be made to secure statistical series of deer mice and kangaroo rats from areas of extreme color types. Such studies are best made in the laboratory with electronic equipment.

Color protection, then, is of great value to the species which have become adapted to the area which houses it. But it should be remembered that for this protection to be of advantage, these creatures must stay in those or like areas. Remove them from it and they become like the bitterns of the marsh, which occasionally leave the upright pattern made by the cattails and rushes and attempt their concealment tactics by freezing against the uniform green of swamp bushes. The result is startling. Instead of a perfect blending which conceals the bird from passing boatmen, the bittern stands out almost like black against white, and so plainly visible that it can be seen half a mile away. Some conditioning in the animals must hold them to the areas to which they are adapted.

Doc thus summarizes the value of color studies: "Closer adaptation to the environment is an adaptation factor in evolution. Color variation helps to bring this about. We need to know more about the causes of such changes—how much is due to light, dark, and temperature. How does an animal make color changes and what brings about seasonal variations in color?"

There is much to be done in this field as well as in the study of other than color adaptations; for there are many others. Lack of moisture is counteracted by a search for green and succulent vegetation by animals like jack rabbits; by obtaining moisture from insect food, as in the case of birds and chipmunks; or by the obvious method of living near water holes. Most spectacular of all is the manufacture of water from the breakdown of carbohydrates as performed by kangaroo rats and probably other animals.

Heat is coped with by the habit of retiring to the burrow and remaining inactive when the sun is high, by estivation (summer sleep), or by the adaptation of the body to reduce intake of ultraviolet rays—as is done by the antelope squirrel. The cold, arid condition of winter is met by such methods as migration, hibernation, by changes in the weight of pelage, and by devices which enable the animal to get over the snow more easily.

It should be understood that fitness for its surroundings is not something which each animal learns from its own experience or from living. The individual animal does not experiment and then decide that the most desirable life for it is in the burrow or the tree nest or the corn field or the marsh. Adaptation is genetic, which means that it is hereditary, and ecologists are primarily interested in the hereditary adjustment of an organism to its environment. Adaptation is transmitted from one generation to the other. It is not necessary for each generation of Brewer's sparrows to learn how to construct a nest, nor for a water bird to learn to dive. I have seen a young pied-billed grebe dive and swim under water the first day it was born.

Adaptation helps the animal get along under conditions in which an unadapted creature could not live. It is survival equipment which aids in otherwise restrictive locations.

It is not peculiar to animals alone. Plants have adaptive characteristics. Spines and thorns prevent overgrazing of desert plants; strong oils and other contents make them distasteful to foraging stock. Deep taproots and wide, shallow root systems provide different methods of obtaining moisture in a country of occasional but severe storms in which most of the rain is lost by sudden runoff. Underground runners often provide methods of subsistence. Loss of water is prevented by thick or "varnished" epidermis, small leaves, or leaves which drop early in the season; hairy surfaces cut down the transpiration rate. Desert seeds must last for years, or until a favorable condition arrives. Plants must be able to resist water loss and be quickly responsive to growing weather. Wide dissemination of seeds insures continuance of the species and is obtained by such methods as those of the tumbleweed, which rolls over the land, distributing seeds as it moves.

Desert areas prosper because the plants and animals are conditioned to it. The desert is gray, and gray predominates in the color of the flora and the fauna. They are of this color not through accident, but because the mechanism of adaptation—the adjustment of the species to its surroundings—has fitted, and is fitting, the species to the area in which it is found. Without such adaptations, the species would almost certainly perish; with them, it flourishes, and with such success that it holds to the area and similar areas so tightly that changes are made only with difficulty.

CHAPTER XXIV

The Herps

We were leaving the shore of the old lake bed. Eroded banks of sand and ash stood all about us. Small, half-dried desert plants shivered in the breeze with a sound that reminded me of the crushing of rather crisp tissue paper. Fossils, relics of a time when the country was wet and trees flourished, were plentiful. The morning had been well spent, but it was now noon and time to lay off until the cool of the evening.

There was a flash at our feet as a gray and red object streaked past us.

"I'd hate to have to catch that animal, especially on a hot day like this," I said. "It's really in a hurry. It would be a tough job to get hold of it."

"Not so bad as you'd think," said Doc. "In fact, I'd bet ten to one I could get that fellow with my hands. Come along."

I followed as we walked among the gray rocks and the gray vegetation where the animal had disappeared. I wondered just how Doc would catch the creature; I couldn't figure how he could even find it. He walked about ten paces and then stood still; I stopped behind him. He pointed under the edge of a small bush. There was the lizard, absolutely motionless, looking as lethargic as a turtle. I wondered how long it would remain that way. Doc didn't wait to find out but made two slow steps and approached without any quick movements which might alarm the prey. Then his right hand shot forward toward the object. He had aimed correctly. There was much wiggling but no escape. He held the lizard up for inspection.

"How did you know it would stop that way?" I asked. "When it passed me, it looked like the beginning of a long trip."

"Those fellows are like some auto drivers," observed Wyomin'. "The way they start makes you think they are on a life and death matter; then, when you get a few blocks down the street, you see 'em amblin' along and adjustin' their radio."

I thought it was a leopard lizard, and Doc confirmed it. They prefer hot and dry areas with fine, gravel-free soils, or nondrifting sand which carries sparse vegetation. In some places they are quite abundant and the commonest lizards. They can move swiftly and, like all their kind, they are quickest on hot days. In cold weather they are much more sluggish and rarely seen.

"What do the country people call them?" I asked.

"It's just a lizard to them," said Doc. "They don't pay any attention to the reptiles and the amphibians, the animals that herpetologists specialize on. The reptiles in the state include turtles, snakes, and lizards. The amphibians are salamanders, toads, and frogs. Biologists have nicknamed these two groups 'herps.'

I suppose country people know less about them than they do about any other desert animals."

"It's no wonder," said Wyomin'. "You can't hunt herps for sport. They aren't cute like chipmunks and ground squirrels. They show no interest in man. Nobody ever heard of a herp comin' up to eat peanuts. Wouldn't they make a swell pet? Imagine one of them crawlin' under your blankets to get warm. It would be just like somebody had slipped a piece of ice into your bed. I bet you could feed them for months without them knowin' you or actin' glad to see you."

In some places the amphibians outnumber the reptiles, but there were few amphibians in Owyhee. This is as we would expect, for amphibians, with minor exceptions, spend part of their lives in water. They have smooth, scaleless skins that must be kept moist. Consequently, they live in or near water holes, along streams, and irrigating ditches. The water must be fresh. The group consists of toads, frogs, and salamanders, which are often mistaken for lizards, but they lack the rough or scaly lizard coatings. There are no records of salamanders in the county, although long-toed and tiger salamanders have been found in like localities.

But several toads and frogs are found in the few moist areas. The Hammond spadefoot toad sings loudly during the breeding season in the water holes of the Bruneau sand dunes, and can be found in temporary wet spots in many other places. They live in holes excavated with their hind feet which bear cutting edges for that purpose. The western toad is the commonest in the county and is found throughout in grass and herbs along flowing water. Another

widely distributed toad is the Pacific tree frog which
inhabits not only trees but lives in ponds, among
rocks, and around buildings. There appear to be no
bullfrogs in Owyhee except for a few along the Snake
River. Other species of toads and frogs are the swamp
cricket frog, the Woodhouse toad, the leopard frog,
and the Nevada spotted frog. Their distribution is
wide enough so that, in season, an evening chorus is
to be expected where conditions are favorable. But
among the herps, the reptiles are much more numerous, because they are better suited to the conditions
prevailing in the largest part of the county.

The reptiles breathe by means of lungs during all
stages of their lives, and they possess scaly or leathery
coverings on their bodies. One species of turtle has
been found in Owyhee.

I have always agreed with Wyomin', who says, "To
me, lizards are the most typical desert animals. I
can't help thinkin' they look more like a part of this
dry country than any livin' thing we see."

We think that way, I suspect, because no desert
place is so hot and desolate that you can't see lizards
running around, and looking as if they were in their
proper place. They move swiftly about the sand of
the lower desert and they run as swiftly over the
almost perpendicular rocks of the Bruneau Canyon.
They appear to do well, regardless of how dry the
country is.

The leopard lizard, previously mentioned, is a typical example. It measures between ten and twelve
inches, two thirds of which is tail. Moderately large
round dark spots cover a background of gray or grayish-
brown and give it a leopard-like appearance. The tail
is usually mottled white and dark color but, after

mating, the tail of the female becomes a brilliant salmon red on its undersurface and sides. At that time it is the most highly colored of Idaho lizards. The leopard lizard feeds largely on grasshoppers and other insects. It also consumes other lizards to such an extent that it is regarded as the most cannibalistic known in North America. It hunts actively and will jump into the air for an insect. It is rather vicious and will attempt to bite when captured.

The two to four eggs are laid during the first half of July and they hatch in August. Doc reports seeing many young specimens from two to three inches in length. Once, when he was working on his recording thermometer, they displayed curiosity. When he revolved the drum of the instrument so that it made a humming sound, two young ones ran right up to the instrument.

The foregoing is a rather sketchy idea of the life of one of the nine species of Owyhee lizards. As may be expected, the species vary considerably in size, appearance, and habits. Some climb when alarmed; others seek refuge in crevices or holes. Some prefer rocks; others stay in soft sand. I mention names because they are fairly descriptive of certain characteristics. The tail of the whip-tailed lizard is slender and nearly twice as long as the head and body. The northern alligator lizard resembles its namesake; the name sagebrush lizard indicates a brush-dwelling habit, but this creature merely lives in such areas and seeks escape in burrows; no burrows for the western fence lizard—it retreats only by climbing, and spends its time in fences, around buildings and trees, and even in rocks. The western collared, the northern brown-shouldered, and the short-horned (known as horned toads) lizards have taken their names from their appearance.

The rough and uninviting appearance of lizards is probably the cause of the superstition and untrue tales about them. They are reported to be poisonous when in reality there are only two poisonous species known in the world, one of which, the Gila monster, lives in the Southwest. Their habit, common in some species, of tail shedding when attacked, causes endless comment, and the regeneration of a new tail has been used to justify many a half-baked theory of the possibility of extensive regeneration among mammals.

Next to the lizards in the Owyhee Desert come the snakes. Seven kinds have been taken in the county, all nonpoisonous to humans except the rattlesnakes. The commonest of the Owyhee snakes is the desert gopher snake, which is also the largest. We run across it frequently in cheat grass where it is easily collected. It resents being handled in the wild, but is said to become friendly in captivity. The rarest local species is the long-nosed, of which only a few specimens have been taken. The wandering garter snake can be found usually near water for it is a lover of wet grass, stream margins, and expertly catches frogs and young fish. Doc reports one case where the tables were reversed —he caught a large trout with a small garter snake in its stomach. Occasionally we run across a ring-necked snake, easily identified by the bright yellow on the neck. Then there are the thin and fast travelers, the yellow-bellied and western striped racer, and a diminutive representative of the boas, the Pacific rubber snake.

We see some snakes nearly every day we are in

the field. They go their own way, preying upon their especial type of food, and preyed upon by hawks, owls, badgers, and many other mammals and birds. Their number proves that the desert provides good habitats although they are not, as sometimes thought, resistant to, and tolerant of, extreme heat. They like to sun themselves, but they must retire before the very high temperatures sometimes found. They hunt largely at night because it is cooler and because their prey is available at that time.

There is another snake which we see frequently. It is the rattlesnake, the snake which many people have never seen but which everybody knows—the poisonous snake, the menace to children and animals, the creature whose bite is sometimes fatal. No snake in the United States is so much feared. Many strangers will not go into desert country because of rattlers. The damage done by them is grossly exaggerated. Rumor has it that there are many, many deaths from their bites each year. Doc has consulted the Idaho mortality records and can find no deaths due to rattlers. The only recent death I have heard of was that of a child in the Southwest who was bitten by a young rattler which she had picked up to play with. We have been in the field for many days at a time without experiencing what might be called close escapes. We met one Owyhee sheepherder who had never seen a rattler during sixteen years of herding in higher country.

That does not mean that precautions should not be taken. Rattlers are distributed through the county, except in the higher altitudes, and are common in juniper highlands and along deep river canyons such as the Bruneau and Jarbidge. Early in the season they seek rocks in sagebrush but, when these habitats become dry in the middle summer heat, they will move to places where the hunting is better. They become quite common at that time in the Stoneman Creek meadows and in fields. In August, the hottest part of the summer, they feed mostly at night. At that time we have found that perhaps one in three does not rattle when approached. We are always careful of broken rock areas and of the grass ordinarily occupied by jumping mice in the juniper plateau.

We have concluded that rattles provide no accurate estimate of age. It is generally accepted that one rattle is added at the time of each moult, and the period between moults may vary considerably. Usually, or often, the last few rattle buttons are cracked and could easily be lost. In our experience we have never seen one with more than nine rattles and a button.

I had always wondered how local people, living in snake country, regarded rattlers. How did they like to find a rattler sunning itself on the south side of the house? or in the dust of a corral? or even on the porch? Did they fear them? and were they always nervous about them? Did they consider them a great menace? I asked Wyomin' who had been raised in just such country.

"They don't like them," he answered, "but they don't sit around worryin' about them. They're awful careful to keep things cleaned up so the rattlers can't hurt children—they don't leave any cluttered places where snakes could hide. They kind of learn to keep an eye out for them without even realizin' they are doin' it. The active season for them is not too long, you know. I'd say they regard them as more of a nuisance than a danger."

I talked to a young married woman who had been raised in a dry coulee where the snakes were really numerous, for the ranch was built close to the rim-rock.

"You have to realize that they might be near you any time, and you have to act accordingly. One place I don't like them is in the orchard—they sometimes get in the grass and they're hard to see. But in our coulee the kids go barefoot and not one of them has ever been bitten—maybe it's because we're lucky. People don't like them. They don't like terrible thunder-storms, either. But they don't worry too much about them. I'd say they think the chance of being killed by either is possible but not likely."

I talked to several men who had slept on the ground in the open while harvesting. Every one of them claimed they had found a snake at least once under their blankets, but they did not think it serious enough to carry a cot or hammock. Two of them thought the snakes only got under cover when they were cold and almost inactive.

Wyomin' said that ranchers didn't have any friendly feelings for them. They kill every one they see on the range just on general principles. He added, "One of my cousins said he always found quite a few in one corner of his ranch. He thought there was a den in the rimrock somewhere around and he figured on findin' it and blastin' it with dynamite, but I never heard that he got around to it. I think most every-body would like to get rid of them but, as one rancher said, 'You can't bail out the ocean.'"

How the tourists hate and fear them! Once I heard

a ranger describe the advantages and beauties of a trip to the bottom of the Grand Canyon of the Colorado. When he finished, a woman from Detroit asked, "Are there many rattlesnakes in the canyon?" He said there were certainly some, but the possibility of seeing one on the trail was remote. But she said, "If there's a chance of seeing one single rattlesnake in a county I never go near it."

"She'd better stick to main streets and hotels in desert country then," said Wyomin', "although she might take twenty trips and not see one. It all depends on what you're used to. Autos kill more people in one year in Detroit than have been killed by rattlers in the whole history of the West."

Nobody can claim that a surprise meeting with a rattlesnake is an enjoyable affair. Their menace and hostility and aggressiveness may be only what the scientists call "the defense mechanism of a frightened creature which wants only to be left alone," but they do surprise a person if the meeting is sudden. I have never been especially startled or disturbed on seeing a rattler in the Northwest.

I mentioned that to Doc and added that I had met one in Arizona which gave me a totally different feeling. I was walking in the sand of a dry wash and had reached a place where the floor narrowed to ten feet, with vertical rock bordered by brush on either side.

I was examining a rock wall where I had previously found a rather rare fern. Suddenly a sound came from the sand about three yards in front of me. I knew immediately what it was. Nobody who had ever heard it would forget the nature of that high-pitched whirring. I had listened to it many times farther north, but the intensity of this sound surpassed anything in my previous experience. It came out like escaping steam. It grew stronger as if a valve were opening.

A few feet ahead of me I saw the form of a huge coiled snake with head perhaps a foot above the ground and looking my way. My five-foot staff of ocotillo wood was unfit for attack or protection. I couldn't see a stone big enough to do any good. I couldn't detour, for the wash margins were steep and the brush thorny. Meanwhile the rattle rose and fell in an ominous warning. I was thankful that the rattler, unlike some of the snakes of the Far East, did not attack. The softness of the sand would cut down my speed. But this snake neither advanced nor retreated but lay there with its misshaped, pitted head facing me. I can imagine nothing more evil.

My nerves were a bit shaken, but not enough to prevent me from thinking that I had been treated fairly. I might have continued my watch for ferns and walked right on it. It had merely stood its ground and acted out the historic motto, "Don't tread on me." If the end results could be deadly and its appearance appallingly repulsive, it was only for self-defense.

Wyomin' said, "I suppose a big fellow like that could really jar a man. How long do you think it was?"

"As big as a man's upper arm in cross section, and a foot or so longer than my staff."

"That kind of a situation is a good test of the scientific theory that all creatures have a right to existence," said Doc. "Man has always disliked snakes. Remember in the Bible '. . . cursed thou *art* above all cattle, and above every beast of the field; upon thy belly shalt thou go, and dust shalt thou eat all the

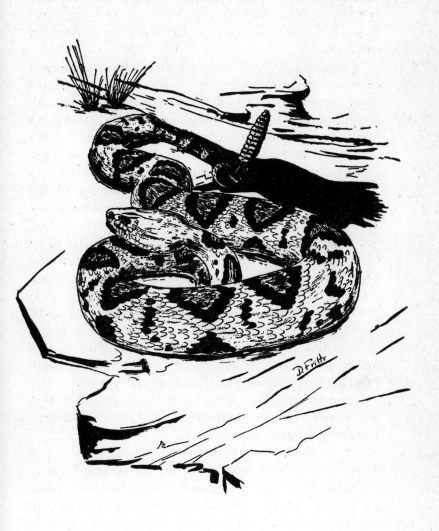

days of thy life: And I will put enmity between thee and the woman, and between thy seed and her seed; it shall bruise thy head, and thou shalt bruise his heel.' "

"I didn't kill it," I said. "I didn't have a weapon even if I wanted to use it. I just stood there and threw small stones until the snake moved into the brush. I got by quickly while I could tell by the noise just where it was. But after that experience I don't believe I ever will be greatly disturbed by the two- or three-footers we see around Owyhee."

Day after day we increased our knowledge of the desert reptiles. We found it interesting, after dealing with mammals of great economic importance, to find out how small an economic factor the herps are. The bullfrogs along the Snake are too scarce to be of any importance to man, and the other frogs and the toads are of benefit only to the herons, cranes, and mammal predators. The lizards, though numerous and great insect eaters, have little influence, beneficial or harmful, on man. The lizards probably contribute heavily to the predator food chains in their areas, although the exact conditions are not thoroughly known.

Once the reptiles were of such importance that one period has been called "The Age of Reptiles." But, as Wyomin' says:

"Well, the herps aren't what they used to be. The seventy-five-foot, thirty-ton babies are all gone. Nowadays no big things the size of Mallett freight engines can jump out at you. The biggest land reptiles in the whole world are in the Far East and are only twelve or fourteen feet long. All that's left in the United States (besides a few alligators and crocodiles) are snakes, and small lizards, and little frogs and toads. There's only one good side to it. It may not be so excitin', but you can walk up a canyon without havin' a five-foot claw wrapped around your neck!"

CHAPTER XXV

The Sheepherder

I sat on the rocks outside our camp and watched the sheep as they fed high on the opposite hills. We were beautifully situated after a week in the hottest part of the desert. We had moved high up into what might be called a vertical oasis. We faced turbulent Jordan Creek and we got our drinking water from a tributary on the north side of our camp. We could have had trout for the catching, if we had wanted to spare the time.

Once the slope in front of us had been timbered, but the silver hunters who discovered the minerals in the Silver City district had exhausted the supply and only scanty growth had returned. Coyotes and cougars had hunted deer in the draws before the miners came. In recent years the government trappers have about cleaned out the last of the predators and the hunters help to keep the deer population down to reasonable limits.

The district had not always been so peaceful. During the mining boom I might have listened to the whine of the saws as men laboriously drove them through the logs, one man on a platform above and the other below in the sawpit after which Sawpit Creek, where we were camped, was named. If I had sat there in those early days, I could have seen the lights of the village on the hill as the afternoon shadows darkened and the miners came home from their day's work. Several thousand people lived in the immediate area, but now probably less than twenty occupied old dwellings in the ghost town of Silver City.

Mining had exhausted the known workings and emptied the town of its inhabitants. A few tourists visited each year and looked over the bleakness of what had been a heavily producing mineral district. There were neither signs of wood chopping nor roads for wood hauling. It was sheep range now. A rancher from the lower district had leased the summer grazing rights. It was his sheep I had been watching. I could hear the dogs now. The animals were coming down for water. The clear, running stream in front of me would soon be disturbed by them. The slopes, sagebrush-covered and high-reaching, were alive with dust-raising, bawling, and slowly moving sheep—a band of ewes whose lambs trailed and mingled their shrill voices with the more mellow sounds of their mothers. The barking of the sheep dogs could be heard as they pushed the slower animals up to the main flock or collected small groups which had tried to stray. The band progressed unevenly but steadily, stopping only when they had reached the water which by now was as brown as thin coffee. Some stopped to clip a clump of grass or to nibble at a bush; others, probably more thirsty, jogged directly to the water. I had watched

it often—the typical scene of aimless and noisy progress which made so many people wonder how a herder could endure the outcry and confusion.

If the herder was annoyed by this babel, he gave
no evidence of it. He leisurely followed the last of
the sheep, walking without a single glance at the rough,
rock-strewn ground. His coat hung on one shoulder,
his flat-top black felt hat was pulled tight over his
forehead and turned down to protect his eyes. He was
a small man who appeared smaller because of the
tight overalls which he wore.

He spoke to me with a curt "Hello" which was
belied by his smile.

He had pulled his smoking tobacco from his front
shirt pocket, but he replaced it when I offered him
one of the two cigars which I had brought along.
We sat down on a flat rock where we could see the
sheep crowding along the stream. As usual, the ones
behind pressed forward until those in front were about
to be forced into the water. Some of them crossed
with a mighty leap which could easily break a leg,
while others, more cautious, waded through the water
they feared and avoided whenever possible. The lambs
milled around in the confusion, crying loudly when
separated from their mothers, trying to suckle when
they found them.

The herder's gaze wandered as if the thought of
sheep was farthest from his mind. He held the cigar
between his front teeth, puffing with deep breaths,
and blowing the smoke out in forcible gasps. His
eyes did not lack brightness nor was there any appearance of weariness in his posture. His voice was low
but clear as he spoke with the slightly slurring accent
of the Basque.

He said, "My name is John Zuloago. I've herded sheep in this district for over fifteen years."

I said, "My name is Frank Haller. You must know the country pretty well, John."

"I can walk the hills when night is darkest or when fog wipes out everything. I better be able to. Miners dug many prospect shafts years ago on these hills. A man who didn't know just where he was could easy fall in."

Now that the sheep were at the water, the dogs thought that their job was temporarily completed. They came for a pat of commendation from the herder; then prepared to rest. Their friendliness amazed me. In town, sheep dogs were sullen and suspicious, often snapping at people who were foolish enough to try to touch them. Here they regarded my association with their master as a proper introduction, for they came close and not only permitted, but asked for, petting.

The heightened sun made shade desirable, so the youngest dog, a brown female of about six months, lay in the shadow of her master and shifted when necessary. The second animal, a yearling of a bluish tinge, found a sagebrush bush just large enough to protect it and, by continual readjustment, managed to keep in the shadow. The third, much larger than the others, could find no bush of sufficient size. I watched curiously and finally a solution was reached when it dug down to the moisture which had dropped during the squall of the night before. Their rapid breathing made me wonder why sheep dogs, even in hot countries, were always long haired; I could not remember having seen one with a short coat.

When the sheep had satisfied their thirst, they be-

gan to scatter. Some of them moved close to the
herder and dogs who paid no attention to them. Evidently the concern of both the man and his helpers
was manifested only when the sheep were in difficulty.
I thought of the antiquity of the calling represented
by the withered little Basque who sat beside me.
Sheep, perhaps procured from wild mountain flocks,
had been the first of men's partly domesticated animals. They could flourish where cattle could not live;
they could be driven by their owners; they moved
slowly so they could be controlled; their pelts furnished warmth, their flesh food, and their skins could
be used for containers. They were really living and
traveling food supplies. Their value was recognized
in the earliest of writings. The Bible constantly re-
ferred to them—Cain had been a tiller of the field,
but Abel was a keeper of sheep who brought the first-
lings of the flocks as an offering to the Lord.

The situation aroused my imagination. This fellow came from close to Bible country. The hills where
his ancestors cared for their flocks must have been
very much like those described in the Scriptures. In
ancient times, sheep tending was one of the most respected of callings, with high obligations. I remembered a quotation used by the minister when he had
preached a sermon for a young lieutenant who had
sacrificed himself for his men: "The good shepherd
giveth his life for the sheep." I had read of the scorn
cast upon shepherds who had fed themselves but had
neglected their flocks. I supposed it was still true:
a shepherd who finds his flock in trouble has to see
it through, regardless of the effort required and the
danger faced. The flocks fed and sheltered their owners who, in return, must furnish all possible protec-

tion and care. Probably it had been the most enduring of man and animal partnerships.

We smoked silently. The absence of wind caused the dust stirred up by the moving animals to hang in little clouds. The temperature steadily climbed. The jaws of the feeding animals made a constant sound. They were too busy to bleat continually as they did while traveling but, now and then, a small group would begin to utter the mixed cries of the ewes and the lambs. The herder, silent and motionless, smoked the shortened cigar which still projected from the center of his mouth. The big dog found the soil beneath him getting too warm and remedied the situation by clawing out the top layer until cool, moist ground was again reached. A brown lizard appeared from under a sagebush and moved back and forth by rapid dashes in the open. The dogs ignored it, although it came close to them.

I watched the lambs about their mothers. Tiny things, long-legged with small heads and tails. They romped, jumping with stiff legs, making little rushes which ended immediately when they found themselves away from protection. They then would return and crook their necks under their mothers' bellies and nurse, their wagging tails showing the pleasure which the warm milk gave them. The stolid ewes continued their feeding as if unaware of the presence of their offspring.

I did not break the silence until the herder's cigar was finished. When he was in the right mood, I wanted to get him to answer some questions. When he carefully extinguished the cigar stub, I asked, "Why is it that every foreign picture of sheep shows the herder with a crook in his hand, but you don't see them around here?"

"I think because in Europe sheep country is rough," the herder said. "Sheep there fall or get pushed into deep cracks. A shepherd can put crook around sheep's leg and pull the sheep out."

An eagle was flying high above them, swinging in great circles and taking advantage of the air currents to soar for minutes at a time.

"Do those fellows bother sheep any?" I asked.

"No eagle ever took lamb from my band. No other bird hurt my sheep. But if cougar start killing, that is bad. Often he takes a sheep. He follows until I can stop him with .30-30. Coyote is worst of all. He kill dozen sheep at one time. Government has to poison and trap and shoot to get rid of him. He always cause trouble. He is wise like everything. If government stop hunting for few months, then there are many again. Dogs are next bad to coyote. When dogs run wild, they make much damage."

There were about two thousand sheep in the band. Two men handled them—one to herd and the other to move camp, pack in supplies, and look after the horses. They used a tent for shelter in the hills. The packer picked up his supplies at the closest point a car could bring them.

"Where do you get your sheep dogs?" I asked.

The herder said that some sheepmen raised their dogs from animals which had been imported, but he thought this was foolish. Such dogs were fine for small ranches where they ran a few sheep without a regular herder, but such training wasn't necessary in the hills. Well-bred dogs weren't always good sheep dogs. You stood almost as good a chance to get a good animal from a litter of any good mixed collie strain, and he thought they were tougher than some of the imported ones.

They did not train them. The pups ran with their mothers and the older dogs and learned that way. Many of them were no good. If they didn't act smart and take to it naturally when they were young, they never did learn and couldn't be used. Sheep dogs didn't have any more sense about quitting than herders. They worked from morning till night, sometimes when their feet were bleeding from cuts and bruises. They never stopped when the band was moving. They never let the sheep stray. He pointed to the big dog; that fellow there had climbed every hill in this country a thousand times. The dog looked up from his depression in the ground and wagged his tail.

"Do you fish much, John?" I asked.

"I try when I first come to America. Then I think following sheep give me enough work without walking up and down rock on crick. I guess I ain't much fisherman, anyway. I don't like to eat fish. Mebbe that why I don't bother to catch 'em."

I thought I would give my right eye to be able to fish some of the streams that this man visited every summer, but I didn't mention it. I turned the subject by pointing to the various kinds of plants about him and asking what kinds the sheep would eat. When the sheepherder said they would eat them all, I pointed to untouched patches of vegetation.

"Sheep act just like people," the sheepherder said. "They eat what they like best and let the rest alone. But each time they feed over the ground the food gets scarcer so that late in summer they'll be eating sagebrush and other plants they pass up now."

The flies were beginning to bother the dogs. Their
tails brushed back and forth to keep the pests moving. Now and then a dog would snap when one
buzzed about its head. Their quiet morning sleep
had ended. For the rest of the day they would be
fighting hundreds of insects which swarmed about.
The pup kept her nose pushed under the coat of
the herder who, without any fuss, pulled it up to
protect her more.

"How long have you been in the sheep business,
John?"

"Always. I come from Spain forty-two years ago
when I was fourteen. I joined relatives in the Northwest. The first summer I went out to help an uncle
with his sheep."

"Do you work the year around?" I asked.

"Yes, except for a month's vacation. That is enough
for anybody. I'm always glad to work again."

"What do you do in winter?"

"I look after the daily winter feeding until lambing. That's early in the year. Then sheepman is
really busy. At first we lambed in the open and some
years that was tough on lambs and many died. But
now they start to build sheds. That cuts losses way
down."

I had seen the little ones in the open and had
watched their unsteady progress and pitiful plight in
a late snowstorm. I could not see how any of them
survived under such conditions.

The herder said sheepmen had improved their
breeding stock and lambing methods until they sometimes got 140 per cent increase. That made an awful
lot of difference to an owner who was getting low
prices.

I noticed that many of the ewes on the hill had twins, and I also knew that the hide or pelt of a dead lamb was often removed and temporarily tied to a twin or abandoned lamb until the mother of the dead one would accept it as her own. Sometimes it was only necessary to rub the lamb against the dead lamb so that the ewe would recognize the scent. The herder said that twins were a big strain to a ewe when traveling, or when grass was poor. He had often carried a lamb under his coat on a stormy day when the young could not keep up with the flock.

I looked at the herder with increasing respect. No wonder that the ancients regarded the shepherds so highly. These men worked alone, on small pay, for periods up to the whole twenty-four hours, and into the next day if necessary. They did everything from carrying weak lambs to helping in their delivery and cleaning their rears to ward off intestinal troubles. They tried to save the weak animals and, if they could not, they skinned them and kept their pelts for their employers. Birth to death did not cover their vigil —it included prenatal care and post-mortem activity. All this was done even though nobody made daily trips to check on them. No foreman supervised their work. Nobody would ever know if they had knocked a sick or weak animal on the head instead of fussing with it. Their code, though unwritten, was an exacting one.

Why, then, did these workers who were so respected in foreign lands meet with small esteem in most sections of this country? It must be because rough living and solitude appealed so little to Americans that they thought no man in his right mind could accept such a job. A man wasted his life if he devoted it to sheep. People thought that a herder who listened to their eternal bleating couldn't keep his reason. Who wanted to live alone in a tent which was continually shifted from site to site on rough mountain slopes? Of the dignity inherent in this care of defenseless animals they knew nothing and probably cared less. Perhaps the herder himself felt the same way; the work was only a job, and the only job he felt competent to fill. I thought that a few more questions might be revealing.

"If you're a churchgoing man you don't get much of a chance to attend while you are herding?"

"I try to go to church in winter, but I can't go other times. I think if a man goes when he can, it is all right."

"Do many of your people still speak their native tongue?"

"A few older men and most of the older women do. The young people don't. Some of them can't understand more than a dozen words."

"Do you remember much about your home?"

"No. I was too young when I left. I remember the white house in which I lived and the sheep country and the hills. All my people handled flocks. The work passed from father to son. That's why Basques can easy get jobs in the United States. All Basques don't make good sheepmen, but people give Basques a trial and most always keep them."

"Were you around in the sheep and cattle wars?" I asked.

"That was before I came from Europe. Trouble starts sometime, but cattlemen and sheepmen know where they belong. They go to law if they have to

—nobody takes a gun and starts fighting. The law says who's right and who's wrong."

"What about poisonous weeds?"

"They are only bad in few places. A careful herder gets along all right most of the time. Alfalfa bloat is worse than poison weed. When you move sheep from dry grass into green alfalfa pasture without watching them close, they can swell up and die."

So, I thought, a sheepherder has to be nurse along with his other duties. He has to be on the job every minute. He can't eat dinner without running the risk of losing some of his charges. He has to do everything but take their temperatures. A sheepherder must love his job to stick to such a continuing responsibility.

"What about night herding?"

"That is not much trouble unless bad weather," the Basque said. "The dogs bunch sheep where they happen to be at night, and they bed down. Unless they are awful hungry, they don't stir much after dark. But they begin to feed at daybreak."

I asked if the settling up of the country affected sheep raising much.

The herder said it did. When the country was open and unfenced it was easy to move sheep from the winter to the summer range. Fencing cut the sheep from feed when they were driving them. They had trouble in finding water, too. They had to keep moving until they could get to open range. They used to lose a good many animals when they took them to the mountains. Always they had trouble. A rancher could sue a sheepman who let his sheep get into his fields. Many of them did not like sheep and would cause trouble. Now they haul them in trucks if they go any distance.

The herder pulled a sack of Bull Durham and some papers from his pocket. He rolled the fattest cigarette that I had ever seen and he lighted it with a sulphur match, the kind that would not be permanently injured by getting wet. They were made by a machine which split the block almost to the bottom so that the matches stuck together but could be torn off as desired.

The sheep were still feeding and I noticed their method of foraging. They did not crop lightly as does a horse, but closer to the ground and with a deeper bite which often pulled out the whole plant if the soil was loose. The fringes of the band were moving steadily uphill, but one or two could always be seen making a short dash for a spot where the feed seemed more promising. The herder's eyes moved here and there as he checked their progress, although he may have been unaware that he was watching the animals. I thought again: this man must have a great love for his job to stick to it in this twenty-four-hour fashion.

"What about shearing?" I asked.

"They shear in late winter. It's really tough then. The sheep usually are brought to an overgrazed place where feed is short. So shearers have to work quick. Then the sheep go through a tank and are dipped to kill ticks. It's hard on them to lose all wool at one time, and they don't get along very well if it snows or there is cold rain. A sheepman is always glad when shearing is over."

I asked what was the easiest time of the year for a herder.

"Summer is best, unless there is cold and much storm. Late fall is worse. The sheep are still high in mountain. Owners don't move them until first real bad weather comes. Heavy snow makes hell. Sheep drift with wind no matter where it takes them. Each minute me and dogs must push them. Sometime they bunch and stand. They don't have any fight. If snow gets a little deep, they try to lay down. Once me and dogs fight for two days to get band off hillside and into little grove which gives some shelter. I never forget that storm. I swear I never go out again, but still I am herding."

I thought that this statement proved my point. Such a man must look at his work as a good nurse might look at hers—service to the weak, labor for the love of the defenseless and that sort of thing. He must regard himself as a protector of these dumb, timid animals which were afraid of everybody but their herder and his dogs. I thought again of the minister who said, "A good shepherd gives up his life for the flock." Was this man beside me the kind of man that the Scriptures had in mind?

I was more curious than ever about this dark and quiet little fellow who smoked such fat cigarettes and lit them with those relics of the past—sulphur matches.

"Were you ever in business for yourself?" I asked him.

"Twice," the man said. "I built up good band and was doing fine till panic came along and prices went so low it cleaned me. I managed to get another band and thought I was all right, but prices broke again. I shipped all my increase to Eastern markets and got check for less than hundred dollars after commissions and freight. I owed bank money and I went broke once more. So I went back to herding."

I thought, that's another proof of the man's love for the work he is doing. Even though he goes broke twice, he just can't keep away from it.

"You certainly must like the game to stick to it the way you have," I said.

The herder looked as if surprised at such a statement.

"You ask if I like sheep business?"

"I know I was foolish to ask," I explained. "A man just couldn't stick to it like you have unless he thought it was the best business in the world."

"I guess you don't understand," replied the herder. "I don't like this job. I had to begin it in America 'cause I didn't know anything else. I stuck 'cause nobody else would hire me. I raised two boys. I would never let them go close to a sheep camp 'cause I didn't want 'em to learn enough to make it easier to get job tending sheep than other work. I didn't like herding when I thought I was making money. When I went broke, I stuck 'cause it was the only way I could feed my family. Once you take sheep to the hills you are good for nothing else. When you get older, you ain't even good for that. And I'm getting old. I don't like sheep business."

He got up and the dogs got up, too. It wasn't because he minded what I had said but because the sheep were scattering too much. The dogs stood beside the herder. They had stopped their panting. Perhaps such rapid breathing when they were resting was just a part of their way of relaxing.

The man did not smile, but he did not have any air of complete discouragement that I thought resembled city disillusionment. In spite of his first unsatisfactory diagnosis, I made another guess at the reason. I've asked him how he liked his work. He told me just how he felt about it. Some men would be crushed in such a position, but this man takes it as a matter of course. Perhaps that's the foreign viewpoint. I suppose he thinks a man has to work whether he likes his job or not. A job isn't supposed to be play; it's what he does to make a living. What's the good of fussing about it?

The sheep had moved out more than the herder liked. He started up the canyon with the dogs at his heels. Clouds were beginning to assemble on the peaks—a promise of a thunderstorm in the afternoon. Now that the dogs had gone, a few ground squirrels left their holes and began to scurry back and forth.

I watched the little man as he walked, hat pulled close to his eyes, denim coat hanging over his left shoulder, legs swinging easily over the rocky ground. The dogs were still at his heels, waiting for the sign or word which would send them bounding up the slopes to bring in the stragglers.

CHAPTER XXVI

Farewell to Fall

We were on the desert on an October day. A few patches of snow whitened the high ridges, but the rest of the country wore a shade of brown that only the dry, desert summer can produce. The vegetation was stiff and rattled when we touched it. The side roads carried inches of soft dust. Superficially, one might have thought it late August had there not been a different feeling in the air—a sharp coolness which did not belong to August. Then, too, the typical summer haze had vanished and the distant landscape stood out clearly.

Fall marked the desert. The absence of Brewer's sparrows and the horned larks and other summer birds confirmed it; they had moved south to a more temperate clime. We saw no ground squirrels; they were hibernating. A few antelope squirrels, active the year round, sped over the dry ground. The coolness of the light breeze caused us to button our jackets. Some cirrus clouds hung high in the air. Present weather conditions were perfect, but there was a warning in the look of things.

Wyomin' spoke. "If we have to make any more trips into the back hills or mountains, we better do it soon. I believe it's gettin' ready to do a little late fall spillin' and, whether it sheds rain or snow, it might hold a man up for a few days if he's unlucky enough to be there when the unloadin' goes on."

"Maybe you're right," said Doc. "But it seems a little early to me."

"Speakin' calendar-wise, you're correct, Doc. But even if they did hand me a M.S. degree, I've lived long enough in desert country to believe in signs, certain kinds of course, and somethin' about this day makes me think that the weatherman has forgotten all about the calendar and is gettin' ready to hand out a package of his own brand. Look at those high clouds racin' in from the west. See how fast they're makin' and how quick they move. They mean weather, or I'm an Eastern dude."

"Maybe you're right, Wyomin'. This is our last trip to the high country and we only have to stay overnight. So we don't have to worry."

"I'm not worryin' any; I was just predictin'. But I know this country well. It's no different from Wyomin'. I know what a few hundred feet of snow piled up will do in the higher districts. It's exactly like a cork in a bottle. It doesn't take up much room, but it stops things from gettin' out."

It was a typical trip to the south—first the lake-bed desert; then the climb up the escarpment to the Owyhee Plateau. But the view was not the summer view, for a light fall of snow had whitened the distant mountains. A few strips of vegetation around us had responded to a recent fall shower and showed green. Twice we saw little flocks of snow buntings, arrivals from the north, which would probably winter in the county. Two ravens left the rocks and uttered their hoarse calls as they flew away.

We reached our destination early and without difficulty. Wyomin' and I set up camp while Doc did his field work. We ate late and retired early so that we could make a daylight start. I awakened during the night to hear the tent ropes vibrating as the tent billowed in the force of a heavy wind. I did not get up. Wyomin' and I had staked the tent with extra care—we knew that even a gale would not disturb it. If the others woke up, they had evidently felt as I did for they stuck to their sleeping bags. When I awoke later, I felt dampness on my face. It gave me an idea of what was going on outside.

We waited until full daylight before climbing out in the morning. No need to fight a storm in the dark. Doc, as usual, was the first man up. He put his head out and looked around.

"Holy Jupiter," he said. "You were right, Wyomin', when you predicted a storm. It has come and it has snowed and it is still snowing. There's four inches on the ground right now, and you can't see a juniper fifty feet away. A few flakes have sifted in, but we did remarkably well."

We cooked a breakfast of good, hot oatmeal and coffee and bacon on the Coleman burner in the tent before we stepped out in the storm. It had become colder. The snow was falling in small, light flakes, not perpendicularly as the heavy snowflakes fall in the coastal woods, but at an acute angle with the ground. Now and then a rush of wind would pick them up and drive them toward the ground again. We had no mufflers, but almost simultaneously we pulled our towels from our packsacks and wrapped them around our necks.

Breakfast had warmed us up. We struck our tent with the speed of long practice, packed our supplies, took a last look about to see that we had forgotten nothing, and entered the car.

Doc's invariable habit of heading the car homeward proved of value here. The ground was snow-covered, but we knew that the road was ten feet away with no intervening rocks or other obstructions. We felt the slight ruts as we reached and turned into it.

Doc and I had driven many times in deep snow— sometimes so deep that the banks on either side were as high as the car. Cascade Mountain roads usually have one high side to show you exactly where you are. But we had seldom driven on open country roads covered by unmarked snow. We learned much about the procedure that morning.

I thought of the way the dune breezes in summer had shifted the sand and had removed all animal tracks as if it had been a huge eraser. The snow was an eraser, but in a different way. The snow does not dig into the ground surface as does the wind. It is a builder which puts down level layers, if there's no wind, and which forms drifts if it is wind-tossed. It lies smoothly in some places and in others it makes hummocks where there were hollows, or it makes long hollows where there were mounds. All the time it affects changes which make it difficult to locate the road exactly.

I had the feeling of being in strange country when we left the trees and came out into the open. Our

course of the day before had been over a brown, winding road in brown country. Now we could see no road—just an expanse of snow, with smoothness broken only by drifts and an occasional snow-covered shrub.

I was glad that I had always let the driver do his own driving. I felt no desire to put on the brakes when we seemed to be skidding, or to swing the wheel when we began to leave the road. I left it all to Doc who was capable of doing a better job than I could do and, while I cannot say that I concentrated on watching the scenery, I will say that as far as Wyomin' and I were both concerned, there was only one pilot and he was in charge.

His job was not an easy one. Unbroken snow stretches are of value only to skiers. How are you going to drive on a road in open country when that mere thread is covered by a sheet which has camouflaged the whole surface? Possibly the weather is clear enough so that you can tell by distant landmarks just where you ultimately want to go. But you might find a thousand twists in the road before you get there, and how are you going to avoid all the little dips and chucks, and the projecting rocks and roots that might tear out the pan? Try it and you will see what I mean. Once somebody has been over it, the driving is easy, but when you try to locate a fourteen-foot strip snaking around in a hundred miles of territory, you have given yourself a job.

Our course was slow and sometimes devious. At times we completely lost the roadbed. Then we were compelled to come to a stop and commence, by trial and error, to locate it again. There was always some slight sign, such as a low place, to indicate that we

had found a rut, or a series of rocks to show that
we were still off. Several times Wyomin' tramped a
short cross trail and solved the mystery. Sometimes
our tire tracks showed a dozen slight changes in direction before we were sure enough to proceed, but we
made it all right. Doc's deliberately slow pace avoided
damage by bumps and ruts, for we eased in and out
without perceptible shock, even if the unexpected
pitches were startling.

"It's like driving in a fog, except that in a fog you
can't see anything very well," said Doc. "Under these
conditions, you get a fair view of everything but the
one that's most important—the road."

"You've said somethin'," said Wyomin'. "It's a real
experience to drive all day under snowstorm conditions. You know you have been someplace."

"City folk can keep away from such roads in winter,
but the rancher who lives there has to put up with
them; he gets plenty of grief," I said.

"He can stick on the ranch," suggested Doc. "You
can see why a lot of back-country ranchers tell me
that they have to hole up with the first snow or bad
rain. The snow drifts high and blocks the way or
the rain makes a bog of some low place, and they're
stuck for the rest of the season.

"The altitude where a rancher lives, or the altitude of the ridges he has to cross to get to the main
road, has a lot to do with his winter travel," said
Doc. "It's amazing how conditions get worse as the
elevation increases. Most low desert snows pass very
quickly, while farther up they may last some time.
At the real high levels snow keeps stacking up until,
in places like Silver City, you can see snowdrifts just
above the town until late August."

The driving constantly improved as the snow abated. Doc continued his slow pace until the road became open and entirely visible. Then, down on the lake-bed desert, we ran into a very light rain.

I thought of the difference in conditions at our camp of last night and our present position. So far, winter had stayed away from the lake-bed country; but the upper levels had bade farewell to fall. The animals of the high country, like the elk and the deer which subsisted largely on browse in winter, would move down far enough to keep out of the snow if it deepened too much. The ground squirrels will be safe in their winter quarters; the pocket gophers, unmindful of the season, will go about their business in the security of their tunnels, only leaving them to burrow in the snow as the drifts deepen. Ravens will exist comfortably in the cliffs and conifers. The beavers will hole up in their lodges or bank burrows and subsist on the stores which they had prepared in the summer season. On the ridges, the coyotes, the weasels, and other predators will glean an uncertain but sufficient living from predation on the lesser mammals.

The lake-bed district below will become increasingly barren and free of visible animal life. The kangaroo rats will be seen occasionally and the jack rabbits will sleep in their open forms and feed on the sage and other browse. Livestock will have been withdrawn from the range and housed in the safety of the canyons, where hay has been stored and shelter is available. A few snow buntings and other winter birds will cheerfully maintain themselves in the desert winter.

But for us, farewell to fall means farewell to desert

activity. Other duties keep us elsewhere, and not until spring comes again will we cross the Snake River and point our car toward Owyhee.

L'ENVOI

Far in the West there lies a desert land, where
    the mountains
Lift, through perpetual snows, their lofty and
    luminous summits.
Down from their jagged, deep ravines, where
    the gorge, like a gateway,
Opens a passage rude to the wheels of the
    emigrant's wagon,
Westward the Oregon flows and the Walleway
    and Owyhee.
                LONGFELLOW, *Evangeline*

Index

N
Marsing
Givens Springs
Snake River
Grandview
Bruneau
Sand Dunes
Cowcreek
Silver City
Boot Hill
De Lamar
Jordan
Creek
South Mt. Range
Ruby
Ridge
Triangle
Hills
Bruneau Canyon
Jack's Cr.
Wickahoney
Grasmere
Creek
Central
Owyhee Highlands
Big Springs
River
North Fork Owyhee
Fairylawn
Battle
Creek
Brakes of the Owyhee